American Book Company

Meeting Standards,
Exceeding Expectations

Dear Educator,

Thank you for your interest in American Book Company's state-specific test preparation resources. We commend you for your interest in pursuing your students' success. Feel free to contact us with any questions about our books, software, or the ordering process.

Our Products Feature	Your Students Will Improve
Multiple-choice and open-ended diagnostic tests	Confidence and mastery of subjects
Step-by-step instruction	Concept development
Frequent practice exercises	Critical thinking
Chapter reviews	Test-taking skills
Multiple-choice practice tests	Problem-solving skills

American Book Company's writers and curriculum specialists have over 100 years of combined teaching experience, working with students from kindergarten through middle, high school, and adult education.

Our company specializes in effective test preparation books and software for high stakes graduation and grade promotion exams across the country.

How to Use This Book

Each book:

*contains a chart of standards which correlates all test questions and chapters to the state exam's standards and benchmarks as published by the state department of education. This chart is found in the front of all preview copies and in the front of all answer keys.

*begins with a full-length pretest (diagnostic test). This test not only adheres to your specific state standards, but also mirrors your state exam in weights and measures to help you assess each individual student's strengths and weaknesses.

*offers an evaluation chart. Depending on which questions the students miss, this chart points to which chapters individual students or the entire class need to review to be prepared for the exam.

*provides comprehensive review of all tested standards within the chapters. Each chapter includes engaging instruction, practice exercises, and chapter reviews to assess students' progress.

*finishes with two full-length practice tests for students to get comfortable with the exam and to assess their progress and mastery of the tested standards and benchmarks.

While we cannot <u>guarantee</u> success, our products are designed to provide students with the concept and skill development they need for the graduation test or grade promotion exam in their own state. We look forward to hearing from you soon.

Sincerely,

The American Book Company Team

PO Box 2638 ★ Woodstock, GA 30188-1383 ★ Phone: 1-888-264-5877 ★ Fax: 1-866-827-3240

Georgia 6th Grade CRCT Test in Science
Chart of Standards

Passing the Georgia 6th Grade CRCT Test in Science

Chart of Standards

The following chart correlates each question on the Diagnostic Test, Practice Test 1, and Practice Test 2 to the Science *GPS Standards published by the Georgia Department of Education*. These test questions are also correlated with chapters in *the 6th Grade CRCT Test in Science*.

Competency Standards	Chapter Number	Diagnostic Test Questions	Practice Test 1 Questions	Practice Test 2 Questions
S6E1. Students will explore current scientific views of the universe and how those views evolved.				
a. Relate the Nature of Science to the progression of basic historical scientific models (geocentric, heliocentric) as they describe our solar system, and the Big Bang as it describes the formation of the universe.	1	1, 2	1, 11	1, 37
b. Describe the position of the solar system in the Milky Way galaxy and the universe.	2	5, 60	2, 55	45, 58

Competency Standards	Chapter Number	Diagnostic Test Questions	Practice Test 1 Questions	Practice Test 2 Questions
c. Compare and contrast the planets in terms of • Size relative to the earth • Surface and atmospheric features • Relative distance from the sun • Ability to support life	2	7, 22, 26	4, 16, 58	3, 8
d. Explain the motion of objects in the day/night sky in terms of relative position.	4	9, 44	8, 24	6, 39, 55
e. Explain that gravity is the force that governs the motion in the solar system.	5	11, 12, 14	10, 20	10, 12
f. Describe the characteristics of comets, asteroids, and meteors.	3	13, 15	27, 44	20, 42

Competency Standards	Chapter Number	Diagnostic Test Questions	Practice Test 1 Questions	Practice Test 2 Questions
S6E2. Students will understand the effects of the relative positions of the earth, moon and sun.				
a. Demonstrate the phases of the moon by showing the alignment of the earth, moon, and sun.	6	16, 59	6, 12, 41	11, 26, 53
b. Explain the alignment of the earth, moon, and sun during solar and lunar eclipses.	7	18, 33	30, 47	13, 14
c. Relate the tilt of the earth to the distribution of sunlight throughout the year and its effect on climate.	8	8, 20, 29	15, 32, 51	16, 24
S6E3. Students will recognize the significant role of water in earth processes.				
a. Explain that a large portion of the Earth's surface is water, consisting of oceans, rivers, lakes, underground water, and ice.	9	6, 21, 23	17, 37	15, 17
b. Relate various atmospheric conditions to stages of the water cycle.	9	24	21, 29	32
c. Describe the composition, location, and subsurface topography of the world's oceans.	9, 10	34, 49	22, 23	18, 28, 56
d. Explain the causes of waves, currents, and tides.	11, 12	27, 42, 58	25, 28	22, 25, 35

Competency Standards	Chapter Number	Diagnostic Test Questions	Practice Test 1 Questions	Practice Test 2 Questions
S6E4. Students will understand how the distribution of land and oceans affects climate and weather.				
a. Demonstrate that land and water absorb and lose heat at different rates and explain the resulting effects on weather patterns.	12	30, 39	9, 31	27. 38
b. Relate unequal heating of land and water surfaces to form large global wind systems and weather events such as tornados and thunderstorms.	12	4, 32	33, 46	19, 31
c. Relate how moisture evaporating from the oceans affects the weather patterns and weather events such as hurricanes.	13	35, 37	36, 38, 43	7, 23, 36

Competency Standards	Chapter Number	Diagnostic Test Questions	Practice Test 1 Questions	Practice Test 2 Questions
S6E5. Students will investigate the scientific view of how the earth's surface is formed.				
a. Compare and contrast the Earth's crust, mantle, and core including temperature, density, and composition.	15	38, 40	40.45	29, 30
b. Classify rocks by their process of formation.	17	41, 53	18, 26	2, 40
c. Describe processes that change rocks and the surface of the earth.	17, 18	36, 43	34, 39	57, 59
d. Recognize that lithospheric plates constantly move and cause major geological events on the earth's surface.	16	17, 26, 56	14, 48, 60	21, 41
e. Explain the effects of physical processes (plate tectonics, erosion, deposition, volcanic eruption, gravity) on geological features including oceans (composition, currents, and tides).	17	31, 45, 48	7, 13, 42	43, 44, 48
f. Describe how fossils show evidence of the changing surface and climate of the Earth.	14	25, 51	50 ,52, 59	49

Competency Standards	Chapter Number	Diagnostic Test Questions	Practice Test 1 Questions	Practice Test 2 Questions
g. Describe soil as consisting of weathered rocks and decomposed organic material.	19	28, 50	53, 56	33., 34
h. Explain the effects of human activity on the erosion of the earth's surface.	18, 20	46, 52	3, 35	50, 52, 60
i. Describe methods for conserving natural resources such as water, soil, and air.	21	10 ,55	19, 49	4, 46, 54
S6E6. Students will describe various sources of energy and with their uses and conservation.				
a. Explain the role of the sun as the major source of energy and its relationship to wind and water energy.	12	47, 57	5, 54	9, 47
b. Identify renewable and nonrenewable resources.	21	3, 54	57	5, 51
All S6CS standards are integrated across the three content domains. Inquiry standards are address within content directed questions.				
		2, 22	2, 4, 16	

PASSING THE

GEORGIA 6TH GRADE CRCT

IN SCIENCE

Written to GPS 2006 Standards

Liz Thompson

American Book Company
PO Box 2638
Woodstock, GA 30188-1383
Toll Free: 1 (888) 264-5877   Phone: (770) 928-2834
Fax: (770) 928-7483 Toll Free Fax: 1 (866) 827-3240
Web site: www.americanbookcompany.com

ACKNOWLEDGEMENTS

The authors would like to gratefully acknowledge the formatting and technical contributions of Becky Wright.

We also want to thank Mary Stoddard for her expertise in developing the graphics for this book.

A special thanks to Marsha Torrens for her editing assistance.

Table of Contents

Table of Contents   iii

Preface   vii

Diagnostic Test   1

Evaluation Chart for Georgia 6th Grade CRCT Test 13

Domain One – Astronomy   15

Chapter 1 Formation of the Universe   17

Chapter 1 Practice Questions 22

Chapter 2 Formation of the Solar System   23

Formation of the Solar System 23
    Formation of the Sun and Asteroids 24
    Formation of the Terrestrial Planets 24
    Formation of the Outer Planets 25
      A League of Their Own 26
Chapter 2 Practice Questions 27
Mini-Review 28

Chapter 3 Comets, Asteroids and Meteors   29

Comets 29
Asteroids 30
Meteoroids 30
    Man-Made "Space Trash" 31
Chapter 3 Practice Questions 32

Chapter 4 Rotation and Revolution   33

Rotation and Revolution 33
    Seasonal Changes 34
Chapter 4 Practice Questions 36

Chapter 5 Gravity and Orbit ... 37
Chapter 5 Practice Questions ... 39
Mini-Review ... 40

Chapter 6 The Phases of the Moon ... 41
The Moon ... 41
Chapter 6 Practice Questions ... 43

Chapter 7 Lunar and Solar Eclipses ... 45
Eclipses ... 45
SCEF (Some Cool Eclipse Facts) ... 46
Chapter 7 Practice Questions ... 47

Chapter 8 The Tilt of the Earth ... 49
The Driving Force ... 51
Chapter 8 Practice Questions ... 52

Domain One Review ... 53

Domain Two – Hydrology and Meteorology ... 57

Chapter 9 Bodies of Water ... 59
Four Earths ... 59
Salt Water ... 60
Fresh Water ... 61
The Water Cycle ... 62
Chapter 9 Practice Questions ... 64

Chapter 10 The Ocean Floor ... 65
Oceanic Trenches ... 66
Seamounts and Mid-Ocean Ridges ... 67
Rift Valleys ... 67
Chapter 10 Practice Questions ... 68

Chapter 11 Ocean Movement I: Tides ... 69
Tides ... 69
SCTF (Some Cool Tide Facts) ... 70
Chapter 11 Practice Questions ... 71
Mini-Review ... 72

Chapter 12 Ocean Movement II: Waves and Currents ... 73
Solar Radiation – Heat from the Sun ... 73
Radiation ... 73
Convection ... 73
Conduction ... 74

Wind and Ocean Currents 74
Chapter 12 Practice Questions 76

Chapter 13 Weather Patterns and Events   77

Weather vs. Climate 77
Weather Patterns 78
    Cold Front 78
    Warm Front 79
    Stationary Front 79
    Occluded Front 79
  Hurricanes 80
Chapter 13 Practice Questions 81
Mini-Review 82

Domain Two Review   83

Domain Three – Geology   87

Chapter 14 Earth's Age   89

Earth's Age 89
  The Law of Superposition 90
  The Fossil Record 90
Chapter 14 Practice Questions 92

Chapter 15 The Layers of the Earth   93

The Earth's Layers 93
  Crust 94
  Mantle 94
  Core 95
  Composition of the Earth 95
Chapter 15 Practice Questions 96

Chapter 16 Plate Tectonics   97

Plate Tectonics 97
  Plate Boundaries 99
  Folding 100
  Faulting 100
Chapter 16 Practice Questions 101
Mini-Review 102

Chapter 17 Rocks and the Rock Cycle   103

Rocks and the Rock Cycle 103
  Igneous Rocks 103
  Sedimentary Rocks 104
  Metamorphic Rocks 104
  The Rock Cycle 104
Volcanic Activity 105

Chapter 17 Practice Questions 106

Chapter 18 Weathering and Erosion   107

Weathering 107
Erosion 108
Chapter 18 Practice Questions 110

Chapter 19 Soil Formation and Composition   111

Chapter 19 Practice Questions   113
Mini-Review   114

Chapter 20 The Effects of Human Activity   115

Logging 115
Building 115
Mining...116
Farming 117
Mini-Review 117
Chapter 20 Practice Questions 118

Chapter 21 Resource Use   119

Resource Use..119
Chapter 21 Practice Questions 121
Mini-Review 122

Domain Three Review   123

Post Test 1   129

Post Test 2   141

Index   151

Preface

The Georgia 6th Grade CRCT Test in Science will help students who are learning or reviewing material for the Georgia test that is now required for each gateway or benchmark course. **The materials in this book are based on the Georgia Performance Standards as published by the Georgia Department of Education**.

This book contains several sections. These sections are as follows: 1) General information about the book; 2) A Diagnostic Test and Evaluation Chart; 3) Domains/Chapters that teach the concepts and skills to improve readiness for Georgia 6th grade CRCT test in Science; 4) Two Practice Tests. Answers to the tests and exercises are in a separate manual. The answer manual also contains a Chart of Standards for teachers to make a more precise diagnosis of student needs and assignments.

We welcome comments and suggestions about the book. Please contact us at

American Book Company
PO Box 2638
Woodstock, GA 30188-1383

Toll Free: 1 (888) 264-5877
Phone: (770) 928-2834
Fax: (770) 928-7483
Web site: www.americanbookcompany.com

About the Author

Liz A. Thompson holds a B.S. in Chemistry and an M.S. in Analytical Chemistry, both from the Georgia Institute of Technology. Research conducted as both an undergraduate and graduate student focused on the creation and fabrication of sensors based on conducting polymers and biomolecules. Post graduate experience includes work in radioanalytical chemistry. Her publications include several articles in respected scientific journals, as well as authorship of two chapters in the textbook *Radioanalytical Chemistry* (in press). At every educational level, Mrs. Thompson has enjoyed teaching, tutoring and mentoring students in the study of science.

American Book Company

*Meeting Standards,
Exceeding Expectations*

PREPARE FOR YOUR END OF COURSE AND EXIT EXAMS!

Let us Diagnose your needs and Provide instruction with our EASY TO USE books!

tutor **Vista**

World Class Tutoring,
A Click Away

Through a unique partnership with **TutorVista**, American Book Company now offers a **Diagnostic Test** that students can take **On-Line**. Test results are e-mailed to the teacher and the student and are graded with references to chapters in our book that will help reinforce the areas that are missed. It's 100% free, it takes the work out of hand grading, and it provides a specific prescription for improving students' performance on state and national assessments.

SIMPLY FOLLOW THESE 3 STEPS:

1 Teachers, provide students with the book's ISBN number and your e-mail address. Then have them go to **www.americanbookcompany.com/tutorvista** and take the FREE On-Line Diagnostic Test.

2 Teachers, determine the best way to use the Diagnostic Test results for your students and classes.

3 Students can use their FREE 2 HOUR TutorVista session to address specific needs and maximize their learning.

We are very excited about this new avenue for test preparation and hope you join us in this opportunity to improve student learning. If you have any questions about TutorVista or the processes explained above, please feel free to contact a customer representative by e-mail at **info@tutorvista.com** or by phone at **1-866-617-6020**.

You may also go to **www.americanbookcompany.com/tutorvista/diagnostic** for ideas and suggestions on how to effectively use this service for students and schools.

Georgia 6th Grade Science CRCT Diagnostic Test

General Instruction

Today you will be taking a test modeled after the Science Criterion-Reference Competency Test. The Science test consists of multiple-choice questions. A sample question is shown below.

There are several important things to remember.

- Read each question carefully and think about the answer.

- Answer all questions on your answer sheet.

- For each question, choose the best answer, and completely fill in the circle in the space provided on your answer sheet.

- If you do not know the answer to a question, skip it and go on. You may return to it later if you have time.

- If you finish the section of the test that you are working on early, you may review your answers in that section only. You may not review another section or go to the next section of the test.

Sample Question

1 "The Earth's oceans can be considered a relatively thin layer of the Earth's overall structure." The oceans are a thin layer as compared to

A. the Earth's core.

C. the mantle.

B. the continental crust.

D. all the above.

1. Ⓐ Ⓑ Ⓒ Ⓓ

Diagnostic Test   **Answer Sheet**

Name: _____

Section 1

1. Ⓐ Ⓑ Ⓒ Ⓓ
2. Ⓐ Ⓑ Ⓒ Ⓓ
3. Ⓐ Ⓑ Ⓒ Ⓓ
4. Ⓐ Ⓑ Ⓒ Ⓓ
5. Ⓐ Ⓑ Ⓒ Ⓓ
6. Ⓐ Ⓑ Ⓒ Ⓓ
7. Ⓐ Ⓑ Ⓒ Ⓓ
8. Ⓐ Ⓑ Ⓒ Ⓓ
9. Ⓐ Ⓑ Ⓒ Ⓓ
10. Ⓐ Ⓑ Ⓒ Ⓓ
11. Ⓐ Ⓑ Ⓒ Ⓓ
12. Ⓐ Ⓑ Ⓒ Ⓓ
13. Ⓐ Ⓑ Ⓒ Ⓓ
14. Ⓐ Ⓑ Ⓒ Ⓓ
15. Ⓐ Ⓑ Ⓒ Ⓓ
16. Ⓐ Ⓑ Ⓒ Ⓓ
17. Ⓐ Ⓑ Ⓒ Ⓓ
18. Ⓐ Ⓑ Ⓒ Ⓓ
19. Ⓐ Ⓑ Ⓒ Ⓓ
20. Ⓐ Ⓑ Ⓒ Ⓓ
21. Ⓐ Ⓑ Ⓒ Ⓓ

22. Ⓐ Ⓑ Ⓒ Ⓓ
23. Ⓐ Ⓑ Ⓒ Ⓓ
24. Ⓐ Ⓑ Ⓒ Ⓓ
25. Ⓐ Ⓑ Ⓒ Ⓓ
26. Ⓐ Ⓑ Ⓒ Ⓓ
27. Ⓐ Ⓑ Ⓒ Ⓓ
28. Ⓐ Ⓑ Ⓒ Ⓓ
29. Ⓐ Ⓑ Ⓒ Ⓓ
30. Ⓐ Ⓑ Ⓒ Ⓓ

Section 2

31. Ⓐ Ⓑ Ⓒ Ⓓ
32. Ⓐ Ⓑ Ⓒ Ⓓ
33. Ⓐ Ⓑ Ⓒ Ⓓ
34. Ⓐ Ⓑ Ⓒ Ⓓ
35. Ⓐ Ⓑ Ⓒ Ⓓ
36. Ⓐ Ⓑ Ⓒ Ⓓ
37. Ⓐ Ⓑ Ⓒ Ⓓ
38. Ⓐ Ⓑ Ⓒ Ⓓ
39. Ⓐ Ⓑ Ⓒ Ⓓ
40. Ⓐ Ⓑ Ⓒ Ⓓ

41. Ⓐ Ⓑ Ⓒ Ⓓ
42. Ⓐ Ⓑ Ⓒ Ⓓ
43. Ⓐ Ⓑ Ⓒ Ⓓ
44. Ⓐ Ⓑ Ⓒ Ⓓ
45. Ⓐ Ⓑ Ⓒ Ⓓ
46. Ⓐ Ⓑ Ⓒ Ⓓ
47. Ⓐ Ⓑ Ⓒ Ⓓ
48. Ⓐ Ⓑ Ⓒ Ⓓ
49. Ⓐ Ⓑ Ⓒ Ⓓ
50. Ⓐ Ⓑ Ⓒ Ⓓ
51. Ⓐ Ⓑ Ⓒ Ⓓ
52. Ⓐ Ⓑ Ⓒ Ⓓ
53. Ⓐ Ⓑ Ⓒ Ⓓ
54. Ⓐ Ⓑ Ⓒ Ⓓ
55. Ⓐ Ⓑ Ⓒ Ⓓ
56. Ⓐ Ⓑ Ⓒ Ⓓ
57. Ⓐ Ⓑ Ⓒ Ⓓ
58. Ⓐ Ⓑ Ⓒ Ⓓ
59. Ⓐ Ⓑ Ⓒ Ⓓ
60. Ⓐ Ⓑ Ⓒ Ⓓ

PLEASE GO ON TO THE NEXT PAGE ⟶

Science Section 1

Use the illustration to answer the question

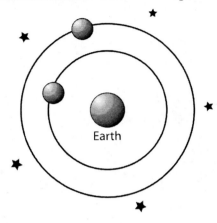

Earth

1. The illustration above represents a   S6E1a
   theory about the solar system. Which
   of the following theories best describes the
   illustration?

   A. Heliocentric theory

   B. Egocentric theory

   C. Geocentric theory

   D. Paleocentric theory

2. Copernicus defended the   S6CS1b, S6CS8c,
   heliocentric theory. Which   S6E1a
   of the following statements
   most accurately describes how Galileo
   furthered this idea?

   A. Galileo invented the telescope.

   B. Galileo observed that moons orbited
   around Jupiter.

   C. Galileo observed that the Moon revolved
   around the Earth.

   D. Galileo discovered Jupiter.

3. Renewable resources are   S6E6b

   A. resources that will replenish themselves.

   B. resources that will not replenish themselves.

   C. resources that may run out in the future.

   D. resources that are in danger of being lost
   forever.

4. Global winds   S6E4b

   A. blow in constant predictable patterns.

   B. blow constantly in unpredictable patterns.

   C. blow periodically in predictable patterns.

   D. blow periodically in unpredictable patterns.

5. An astronomical unit is equal to   S6E1b

   A. the distance light travels in a year.

   B. the average distance between the Sun and
   the Earth.

   C. the distance across the Milky Way.

   D. the diameter of the Milky Way.

6. Which units are BEST for describing   S6E3a
   the area of the ocean?

   A. m   C. km

   B. m^2 D. km^2

7. What makes Uranus and Neptune appear to glow blue-green?   S6E1c

A. atmospheric carbon dioxide

B. ice caps

C. atmospheric methane

D. gaseous centers

8. At what angle is Earth tilted toward the Sun at the summer solstice in the southern hemisphere?   S6E2c

A. 23.5° away from the Sun

B. 47.0° away from the Sun

C. 23.5° toward the Sun

D. 47.0° toward the Sun

9. What makes it appear as if the Sun rises from the east and sets in the west?   S6E1d

A. the revolution of the Earth

B. the revolution of the Sun

C. the rotation of the Earth

D. the rotation of the Sun

10. Which method is used to conserve soil?   S6E5j

A. legume crop rotation

B. filtation ponds

C. terracing

D. dams

11. Which of the following shapes best describes the Earth's orbit around the Sun?   S6E1e

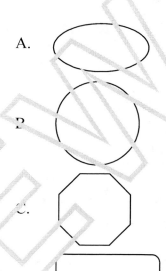

A.

B.

C.

D.

Use the illustration below to answer question 12.

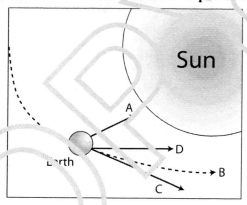

12. Which lettered line on the diagram above represents what would happen if gravity did not act on the Earth?   S6E1e

A. Line C   C. Line A

B. Line B   D. Line D

PLEASE GO ON TO THE NEXT PAGE ⟶

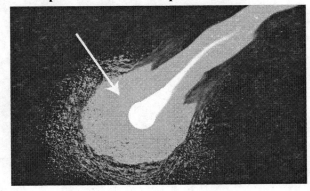

13. The arrow is pointing to the atmosphere around a comet's nucleus. What is that area called?   S6E1f

    A. the tail   C. the center

    B. the head   D. the coma

14. If Earth orbits the Sun at 107,000 miles per hour, why doesn't it spin out of the solar system?   S6E1e

    A. The Sun's gravity keeps it in orbit.

    B. The Earth's inertia keeps it in orbit.

    C. The Earth's weight keeps it from spinning out of the solar system.

    D. The Sun's inertia keeps it in orbit.

15. What usually happens when a meteoroid hits the Earth's atmosphere?   S6E1f

    A. The meteoroid always falls to the Earth.

    B. The meteoroid burns up and can become a shooting star.

    C. The meteoroid explodes.

    D. Meteoroids stay in the asteroid belt and do not approach the Earth.

16. Which of the following best describes the correct phases of the Moon?   S6E2a

    A. first quarter, waxing gibbous, waxing crescent, new moon

    B. waning gibbous, waxing crescent, full moon, new moon

    C. new moon, waxing crescent, waning gibbous, full moon

    D. first quarter, waning crescent, waxing gibbous, new moon

17. Fossils of the same age and from the same species of animal are found on two different continents. This discovery supports which idea?   S6E5e

    A. Heliocentric theory

    B. Continental drift theory

    C. Paleocentric theory

    D. Evolutionary theory

18. What causes a lunar eclipse?   S6E2b

    A. The Moon passes between the Sun and the Earth.

    B. The Earth passes between the Moon and the Sun.

    C. The Sun passes between the Moon and the Earth.

    D. An asteroid passes between the Moon and the Earth.

Use the illustration to answer question 19.

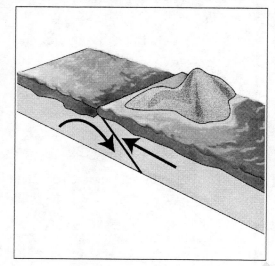

19. What is featured in this illustration? S6E5e

    A. a divergent boundary

    B. folding

    C. a subduction zone

    D. a transform boundary

20. About how many days after the S6E2c
    spring equinox will the fall equinox
    occur?

    A. 90 days   C. 270 days

    B. 180 days   D. 360 days

21. If the Earth's oceans contain 35 S6E3a
    grams of salt per kilogram of water,
    what is the percent salinity of the oceans?

    A. 0.035%   C. 3.5%

    B. 0.35%   D. 35%

22. Which of the following correctly S6CS5a,
    lists the "gas giants" in order from S6E1c
    smallest to largest?

    A. Saturn, Jupiter, Neptune, Uranus

    B. Neptune, Uranus, Jupiter, Saturn

    C. Neptune, Uranus, Saturn, Jupiter

    D. Uranus, Saturn, Jupiter, Neptune

23. The surface area of the Pacific Ocean S6E3c
    is 165 million km^2. The surface area
    of the Indian Ocean is about 73 million km^2.
    The surface area of the Atlantic Ocean is

    A. greater than 165 million km^2.

    B. less than 73 million km^2.

    C. between 73 and 100 million km^2.

    D. between 100 and 165 million km^2.

24. What processes change liquid water S6E3b
    into water vapor in the water cycle?

    A. precipitation and condensation

    B. sublimation and evaporation

    C. evaporation and condensation

    D. evaporation and transpiration

25. You find the fossil of several S6E5g
    alligators during an Arctic
    expedition. What reasonable conclusion
    could you reach?

    A. The area was once much colder.

    B. The area was once much warmer.

    C. Alligators once preferred freezing temperatures.

    D. Alligators were unable to swim at the time the fossil was formed.

PLEASE GO ON TO THE NEXT PAGE ⟶

26. Which of the following planets listed is smaller in size relative to the Earth?   S6E1c

   A. Jupiter
   C. Mercury
   B. Saturn
   D. Neptune

27. When the solar and lunar tidal effects cancel each other   S6E3d

   A. spring tides result.

   B. neap tides result.

   C. a full moon is out.

   D. a new moon is out.

28. Which process is PRIMARILY responsible for the creation of very young soil?   S6E5b

   A. chemical degradation

   B. weathering

   C. decay of plants and animals

   D. creation of organic matter

29. The Sun's rays strike Earth at 90° at the equator during   S6E2c

   A. the summer solstice and autumnal equinox.

   B. the winter solstice and the vernal equinox.

   C. the summer solstice and the winter solstice.

   D. the autumnal equinox and the vernal equinox.

30. At night, the land cools more quickly than the sea. If the temperature of the land drops below the temperature of the sea surface, the air pressure over land is higher than the air pressure over the sea. Which arrow best represents the direction of a land breeze?   S6E4a

A.

B.
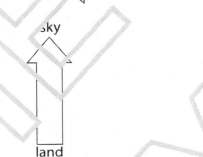

C.
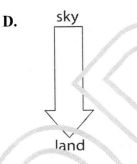

D.

Please STOP!

Do not go on to the next page!

Section 2

31. Which ocean was created by the spreading of South America and Africa?   S6E5f

   A. Atlantic Ocean   C. Indian Ocean

   B. Pacific Ocean   D. Arctic Ocean

32. Two air masses meet. Which of the following conditions will NOT influence the formation of a storm?   S6E4b

   A. differences in moisture

   B. differences in air pressure

   C. differences in temperature

   D. differences in speed

33. During what phase of the moon cycle can a solar eclipse occur?   S6E2b

   A. full moon

   B. first quarter

   C. third quarter

   D. new moon

34. What do sea plants need to survive?   S6E3c

   A. dissolved oxygen

   B. dissolved salts

   C. dissolved minerals

   D. dissolved carbon dioxide

Use the illustration to answer question 35

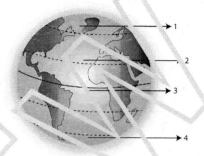

35. What numbered area of the Earth's oceans spawns all tropical storms?   S6E4c

   A. 1   B. 2   C. 3   D. 4

36. Which statement below is the BEST example of chemical weathering?   S6E5d

   A. Limestone gravestones in Georgia dissolve in acid rain.

   B. Stone Mountain in Georgia breaks apart in large sheets due to rock expansion and erosion known as exfoliation.

   C. Wind causes the formation of arches in the rocks at Big South Fork in Tennessee.

   D. Running water carves a valley through a mountain range over millions of years.

37. If you were in an airplane above a hurricane in the Northern Hemisphere, in what direction would the storm be moving?   S6E4c

   A. North

   B. South

   C. North and/or East

   D. South and/or East

PLEASE GO ON TO THE NEXT PAGE ⟶

38. In which of Earth's layers would you expect to find solid rock? S6E5a

   A. mantle   C. crust

   B. guyot   D. outer core

39. Which statement best describes the effect of solar radiation on the Earth? S6E4a

   A. It damages the Earth.

   B. It causes the air, land and water to heat up.

   C. It is not visible, so it does not damage the Earth.

   D. It causes the air to heat up, but not the land or water.

40. The Moho, discovered by Andrija Mohorovicic, is the S6E5a

   A. boundary between the outer and inner core.

   B. boundary between the outer core and the mantle.

   C. boundary between the mantle and the crust.

   D. boundary between the outer core and crust.

41. Which of the following is **NOT** necessary to form metamorphic rocks? S6E5c

   A. sediments   C. pressure

   B. heat   D. chemical reactions

Use the illustration to answer question 42.

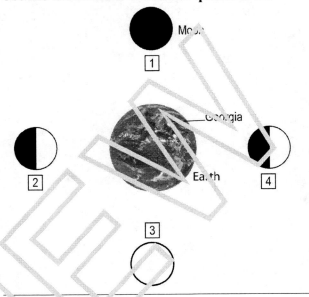

42. Which positions of the Moon represent when spring tide will occur in Savannah, Georgia? S6E3d

   A. 1 and 3   C. 2 and 4

   B. 1 and 2   D. 3 and 4

43. Which shape below **BEST** describes the shape of a valley or canyon created by a river? S6E5d

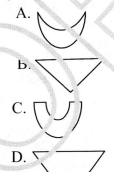

44. Rotation can be considered a measure of _____. S6E1d

   A. time   C. volume

   B. distance   D. mass

45. What type of current is responsible for the movement of Earth's lithospheric plates? S6E5f

   A. wind driven current

   B. thermohaline current

   C. convection current

   D. gulf stream current

46. Clear-cutting is a process used MAINLY by the S6E5i

   A. logging industry.

   B. mining industry.

   C. farming industry.

   D. retail industry.

47. What is the source of all energy on Earth? S6E6a

   A. the Moon

   B. the Earth's rotation

   C. the Sun

   D. man-made energy

48. In 1960, Harry Hess stated his hypothesis that the seafloor was spreading from cracks in the ocean floor from which magma oozes, then hardens. If his hypothesis is correct, what does that mean for rock found 1,000 km from the crack? S6E5f

   A. The rock farther away from the crack is younger than the rock closer to the crack.

   B. The rock is the same age no matter how far away from the crack.

   C. The rock farther away from the crack is composed of different material than rock closer to the crack.

   D. The rock farther away from the crack is older than the rock closer to the crack.

49. Which of the following list the world's primary oceans from smallest to largest? S6E3c

   A. Indian Ocean, Atlantic Ocean, Pacific Ocean

   B. Atlantic Ocean, Indian Ocean, Pacific Ocean

   C. Pacific Ocean, Atlantic Ocean, Indian Ocean

   D. Atlantic Ocean, Pacific Ocean, Indian Ocean

Use the illustration to answer question 50

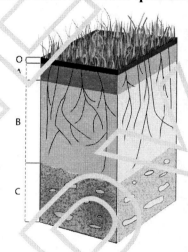

50. Which horizon includes both organic material AND insects and burrowing animals? S6E5h

   A. Horizon O   C. Horizon B

   B. Horizon A   D. Horizon C

PLEASE GO ON TO THE NEXT PAGE ⟶

51. If you found a fossil of a seashell on   S6E5g
top of Brasstown Bald in the
mountains of North Georgia, you could
hypothesize that

   A. the area was once under water.

   B. ancient shells were transported by moving glaciers.

   C. the climate in the past must have been
   colder.

   D. the area was once much higher.

52. Erosion is the   S6E5i

   A. movement of water from one place to
   another.

   B. weathering of rock.

   C. movement of soil from one place to
   another.

   D. creation of topsoil.

Use the following diagram to answer question 53

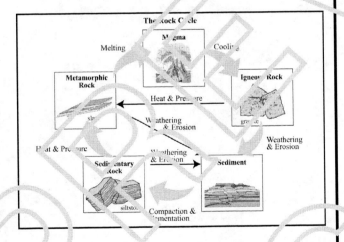

53. Which type of rock weathers to form   S6E5c
sediment?

   A. igneous

   B. sedimentary

   C. metamorphic

   D. All rock types can weather to form sediment.

54. Which of the following is considered   S6E6b
a nonrenewable resource?

   A. wood   C. petroleum

   B. fish   D. water

Use the graph to answer question 55

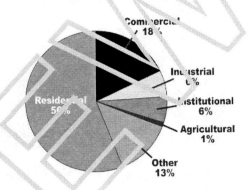

55. According to this chart, residential   S6E5j
water use accounts for over half of
the water used in the United States. Which of
the following is NOT considered residential
water use?

   A. using water to cool turbines

   B. using water for flushing toilets

   C. using water for cleaning

   D. using water for cooking

56. Knowing where lithospheric plates   S6E5e
meet can help scientists predict where

   A. hurricanes and volcanoes may occur.

   B. volcanoes may occur.

   C. volcanoes and earthquakes may occur.

   D. earthquakes may occur.

57. If transpiration describes how water evaporates from plants, which of the following words describes evaporation from both the Earth and from plants? S6E6a

   A. planspiration

   B. evapotranspiration

   C. earthspiration

   D. waterevospiration

58. Which of the following factors is **NOT** responsible for creating waves? S6E3d

   A. Sun   C. heavy rain

   B. wind   D. earthquake

59. Which of the following BEST describes how the phases of the Moon are created? S6E2a

   A. The Moon orbits the Sun.

   B. The Earth casts shadows on the Moon.

   C. The Moon creates its own light.

   D. The Moon orbits the Earth.

60. Where in the Milky Way can our solar system be found? S6E1b

   A. on one of the outer arms of the galaxy

   B. in the center of the galaxy

   C. on the outskirts of the galaxy

   D. our solar system is not located in the Milky Way.

Please STOP!

Do not go on to the next page!

EVALUATION CHART FOR GEORGIA 6TH GRADE CRCT TEST

Directions: On the following chart, circle the question numbers that you answered incorrectly, and evaluate the results. These questions are based on the Georgia Performance Standards for Science. Then turn to the appropriate topics (listed by chapters), read the explanations, and complete the exercises. Review other chapters as needed. Finally, complete the practice test(s) to assess your progress and further prepare you for the *Georgia 6th Grade CRCT Test*.

*Note:Some question numbers will appear under multiple chapters because those questions require demonstration of multiple skills.

Chapters	Diagnostic Test Question
1. Formation of the Universe	1, 2
2. Formation of the Solar System	5, 7, 22, 26, 60
3. Comets, Asteroids, and Meteors	13, 15
4. Rotation and Revolution	9, 44
5. Gravity and Orbit	11, 12, 14
6. The Phases of the Moon	16, 59
7. Lunar and Solar Eclipses	18, 33
8. The Tilt of the Earth	8, 20, 29
9. Bodies of Water	6, 21, 23, 24, 34, 49
10. The Ocean Floor	34, 49
11. Ocean Movement I: Tides	27, 42, 58
12. Ocean Movement II: Waves and Currents	4, 27, 30, 32, 39, 42, 47, 57, 58
13. Weather Patterns and Events	35, 37
14. Earth's Age	25, 51
15. The Layers of the Earth	38, 40
16. Plate Tectonics	17, 19, 36
17. Rocks and Rock Cycle	31, 36, 41, 43, 45, 48, 53
18. Weathering and Erosion	31, 45, 46, 48, 52
19. Soil Formation and Composition	28, 50
20. The Effect of Human Activity	46, 52
21. Resource Use	3, 10, 54, 55

Domain One
Astronomy

DOMAIN ONE COVERS:

Chapter 1 – Formation of the Universe

Chapter 2 – Formation of the Solar System

Chapter 3 – Comets, Asteroids, and Meteors

Chapter 4 – Rotation and Revolution

Chapter 5 – Gravity and Orbit

Chapter 6 – The Phases of the Moon

Chapter 7 – Lunar and Solar Eclipses

Chapter 8 – The Tilt of the Earth

Chapter 1
Formation of the Universe

GEORGIA 6TH GRADE CRCT IN SCIENCE STANDARDS COVERED IN THIS CHAPTER INCLUDE:

S6E1a	Relate the Nature of Science to the progression of basic historical scientific models (geocentric, heliocentric) as they describe our solar system, and the Big Bang as it describes the formation of the universe.

People have wondered about the origin of the universe since — well, since they have been able to wonder! Some astronomers believe that about 13.7 billion years ago, a dense, hot, super-massive ball of material exploded with tremendous force, marking the beginning of the formation of the universe. This theory is known as the **Big Bang**. Immediately following the explosion, the expansion of material allowed for a slight cooling. At this point, the basic atomic (**nuclear**) particles called **protons** and **neutrons** began to form within one second following the explosion. Over time, atoms of hydrogen and helium (the simplest and lightest elements) formed, and the first known conversion of energy into matter had been completed.

During the first billion years or so, hydrogen expanded out into the nothingness, forming enormous clouds. The **rate** of expansion (that is, how fast it happened) was important. If the universe had expanded more rapidly, only hydrogen would have formed. If the universe had expanded at a less rapid pace, more complex elements would have had time to form, and the universe would today be made up of mostly heavy elements. (That is, the elements placed lower on the **Periodic Table**.)

THE PERIODIC TABLE OF THE ELEMENTS

Noble Gases 18 VIIIA

	1 IA	2 IIA	3 IIIB	4 IVB	5 VB	6 VIB	7 VIIB	8 VIIIB	9 VIIIB	10 VIIIB	11 IB	12 IIB	13 IIIA	14 IVA	15 VA	16 VIA	17 VIIA	18 VIIIA
1	1 H Hydrogen 1.0079																	2 He Helium 4.0026
2	3 Li Lithium 6.941	4 Be Beryllium 9.01218											5 B Boron 10.81	6 C Carbon 12.011	7 N Nitrogen 14.0067	8 O Oxygen 15.9994	9 F Fluorine 18.998403	10 Ne Neon 20.179
3	11 Na Sodium 22.9898	12 Mg Magnesium 24.305											13 Al Aluminum 26.98	14 Si Silicon 28.0855	15 P Phosphorus 30.97376	16 S Sulfur 32.06	17 Cl Chlorine 35.453	18 Ar Argon 39.948
4	19 K Potassium 39.0983	20 Ca Calcium 40.08	21 Sc Scandium 44.9559	22 Ti Titanium 47.90	23 V Vanadium 50.941	24 Cr Chromium 51.996	25 Mn Manganese 54.9381	26 Fe Iron 55.847	27 Co Cobalt 58.9332	28 Ni Nickel 58.69	29 Cu Copper 63.546	30 Zn Zinc 65.38	31 Ga Gallium 69.723	32 Ge Germanium 72.61	33 As Arsenic 74.9216	34 Se Selenium 78.96	35 Br Bromine 79.904	36 Kr Krypton 83.80
5	37 Rb Rubidium 85.4678	38 Sr Strontium 87.62	39 Y Yttrium 88.9059	40 Zr Zirconium 91.22	41 Nb Niobium 92.9064	42 Mo Molybdenum 95.94	43 Tc Technetium 97.91	44 Ru Ruthenium 101.07	45 Rh Rhodium 102.9055	46 Pd Palladium 106.4	47 Ag Silver 107.868	48 Cd Cadmium 112.41	49 In Indium 114.82	50 Sn Tin 118.7	51 Sb Antimony 121.75	52 Te Tellurium 127.60	53 I Iodine 126.9045	54 Xe Xenon 131.30
6	55 Cs Cesium 132.9054	56 Ba Barium 137.33	57 La Lanthanum 138.9055	72 Hf Hafnium 178.49	73 Ta Tantalum 180.9479	74 W Tungsten 183.84	75 Re Rhenium 186.2	76 Os Osmium 190.2	77 Ir Iridium 192.22	78 Pt Platinum 195.09	79 Au Gold 196.9665	80 Hg Mercury 200.59	81 Tl Thallium 204.383	82 Pb Lead 207.2	83 Bi Bismuth 208.9808	84 Po Polonium 208.98244	85 At Astatine 209.98744	86 Rn Radon 222.02
7	87 Fr Francium 223.01976	88 Ra Radium 226.0254	89 Ac Actinium 227.02779	104 Rf Rutherfordium 261.1	105 Db Dubnium 262.11	106 Sg Seaborgium 263.12	107 Bh Bohrium 262	108 Hs Hassium 264	109 Mt Meitnerium 268	110 Uun Ununnilium 269	111 Uuu Unununium 272	112 Uub Ununbium 277	113	114 Uuq Ununquadium 289	115	116 Uuh Ununhexium 289	117	118 Uuo Ununoctium 293

Lanthanide Series

57 La Lanthanum 138.9055	58 Ce Cerium 140.12	59 Pr Praseodymium 140.9077	60 Nd Neodymium 144.24	61 Pm Promethium 144.91279	62 Sm Samarium 150.4	63 Eu Europium 151.96	64 Gd Gadolinium 157.25	65 Tb Terbium 158.9254	66 Dy Dysprosium 162.50	67 Ho Holmium 164.9304	68 Er Erbium 167.26	69 Tm Thulium 168.9342	70 Yb Ytterbium 173.04	71 Lu Lutetium 174.967

Actinide Series

89 Ac Actinium 227.02779	90 Th Thorium 232.0381	91 Pa Protactinium 231.0359	92 U Uranium 238.029	93 Np Neptunium 234.0482	94 Pu Plutonium 244.06424	95 Am Americium 243.06139	96 Cm Curium 247.07030	97 Bk Berkelium 247.07030	98 Cf Californium 251.079	99 Es Einsteinium 252.08	100 Fm Fermium 257.09515	101 Md Mendelevium 258.1	102 No Nobelium 259.10	103 Lr Lawrencium 262.11

Key:
36 Kr Krypton 83.80
Atomic Number — Symbol — Name — Atomic Mass

Clouds of hydrogen started the formation of galaxies. Within the galaxies, the hydrogen clouds became denser and began to rotate (spin). Hydrogen was converted into other elements through **fusion** (two nuclei join together). As gravity caused the clouds to condense, the temperature rose. The high temperature and density of these rotating clouds caused nuclear reactions; the bodies of gas and dust then became **luminous** (light producing) stars. When the stars were forming, energy and heat came from the conversion of hydrogen into helium. As the temperature of the star continued to rise, helium was converted to carbon and oxygen. At higher temperatures, oxygen and carbon burned to form elements like aluminum, silicon, phosphorous and sulfur. At still higher temperatures, heavy elements such as iron were formed. Just think... one reaction after another, each one being the cause of the next one.

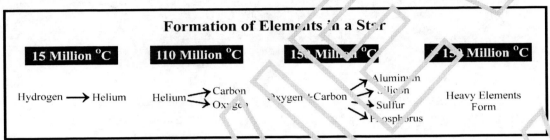

Figure 1.1 Fusion of Hydrogen into Other Elements

The formation of stars led to the formation of **galaxies**. Galaxies are large groups of stars, dust and gas. Galaxies can range in size from 1,500 to 300,000 light years, and they contain an average of 100 billion solar masses (stars, planets, etc.). Our galaxy is called the **Milky Way**, and it has a diameter of about 100,000 light years.

HOLD ON! What is a light year? It is the distance light travels in a year. One light year is about 9.5 trillion kilometers (km)!

The other galaxies in the universe appear to be moving away from the Milky Way; in fact, all of the galaxies in the universe appear to be moving away from one another! This observation is confirmed by recent mapping of "our neighborhood" in the universe and supports the **expanding universe theory**. Since the Big Bang theory has us thinking it all started with one explosion, it makes sense for us to see the universe expand — moving away from us. But this is not exactly the case, as you will see.

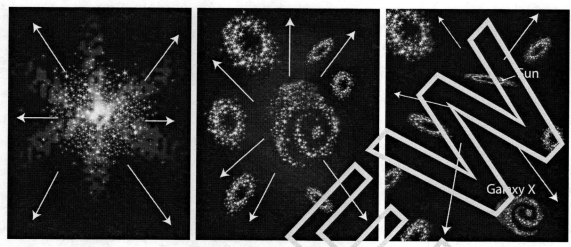

Figure 1.2 The Expanding Universe

Scientists know that the universe is moving. They use the light from stars to determine the direction of the movement. Changes in the color of the stars tell up that some stars are moving closer to the Earth and others are moving away from the Earth. You can think of the universe as a fingerpaint picture that is getting smeared. Let's take a look at the Big Dipper to see what happens.

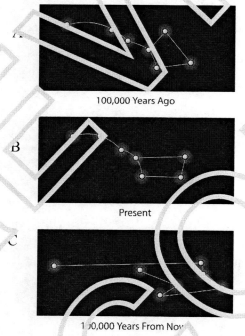

100,000 Years Ago

Present

100,000 Years From Now

Figure 1.5 Transformation of the Big Dipper

Scientists have used mathematical and scientific models to show us what the **Big Dipper** looked like in the north sky 100,000 years ago — that is in Picture A of Figure 1.5. Picture B shows us what the Big Dipper looks like today. Picture C is the prediction of what the Big Dipper will look like 100,000 years from now. Based on these models, the Big Dipper won't even look like a Dipper anymore! If the universe was simply expanding away from us, the Big Dipper would just be getting bigger, meaning that the distance between the stars of the constellation would be increasing. This brings us to the key point — *We here on Earth are NOT the center of the universe!* (In fact, we are not even at the center of our galaxy, as you will see in Chapter 2.)

This fact is in direct contradiction to an important belief held by ancient civilizations, including the Greeks. At that time, most philosophers believed that the Sun, Moon, stars and visible planets all revolved around the Earth. This idea that the Earth is the center of the universe is called the **geocentric theory**. Philosophers that promoted the geocentric (Earth-centered) Theory believed that the Moon, Sun and all the stars moved around the Earth. In opposition to this was the belief that the Sun was actually the center of the universe. Called the **heliocentric theory**, this idea was promoted by a small number of philosophers in ancient Greece. It was not until Copernicus' challenge in the 16th century that the geocentrists began to change their minds.

Copernicus defended the heliocentric theory in his 1542 text *On the Revolutions of Heavenly Spheres*. In 1610, Galileo placed more doubt on the validity of geocentrism with his observations. He discovered and kept track of the four largest moons orbiting Jupiter. They appeared and then disappeared at regular intervals. This led Galileo to believe that the moons were revolving around Jupiter. If this was true, then it was a clear contradiction of the geocentric theory.

As we now know, neither of these theories is correct. The planets in our Solar system revolve around the Sun, but the whole universe does not. In fact, scientists are not at all certain that the universe is a symmetric object (like a perfect circle or sphere) that can even be described as having a center. If that is confusing to you, try this: look up at the sky and pick a big, fluffy cloud. Now try to think "where is the center of that cloud?" It's hard, isn't it? The cloud doesn't have a clear center. The same may be true of our universe.

Chapter 1 Practice Questions

1. What are the two lightest elements?

   A. carbon and oxygen

   B. hydrogen and oxygen

   C. helium and oxygen

   D. hydrogen and helium

2. Astronomers believe that the Big Bang occurred approximately how long ago?

   A. 130 million years ago

   B. 4.6 billion years ago

   C. 10 billion years ago

   D. 14 billion years ago

3. During the normal life of a star, energy and heat come from the conversion of

   A. carbon into helium and some sulfur.

   B. hydrogen into helium.

   C. hydrogen and oxygen into hydrogen.

   D. iron to iron sulfide.

4. Scientists use the light from stars to determine

   A. the shape of the universe.

   B. light coming from the Earth.

   C. the shape of our galaxy.

   D. which stars are moving toward us and which are moving away from us.

5. Which statement best describes the Geocentric Theory?

   A. The Moon revolves around the Earth.

   B. The Earth revolves around the Sun.

   C. The universe revolves around the Earth.

   D. The universe revolves around the Sun.

1. Ⓐ Ⓑ Ⓒ Ⓓ
2. Ⓐ Ⓑ Ⓒ Ⓓ
3. Ⓐ Ⓑ Ⓒ Ⓓ
4. Ⓐ Ⓑ Ⓒ Ⓓ
5. Ⓐ Ⓑ Ⓒ Ⓓ

Chapter 2
Formation of the Solar System

GEORGIA 6TH GRADE CRCT IN SCIENCE STANDARDS COVERED IN THIS CHAPTER INCLUDE:

S6E1b	Describe the position of the solar system in the Milky Way galaxy and the universe.
S6E1c	Compare and contrast the planets in terms of
	• Size relative to the earth
	• Surface and atmospheric features
	• Relative distance from the sun
	• Ability to support life

FORMATION OF THE SOLAR SYSTEM

So, if our galaxy is the Milky Way, what's our solar system called? Well, it is . . . The Solar System. This term specifically refers to our sun, Sol. Other systems have their own names, like the **Alpha Centauri** star system (our closest neighbor). The **nebular hypothesis** suggests that our solar system formed from a vast cloud of dust and gases called a **solar nebula.** According to this hypothesis, the cloud consisted of 80 % hydrogen gas and 15 % helium gas, with the remaining five percent consisting of heavier elements. About five billion years ago, the nebula began to contract (get smaller) under its own gravity and to rotate as a disk-shaped cloud. Through gravitational energy, heavier elements were pulled toward the center of the cloud. The gravitational energy converted to heat energy, causing the center of the spinning disc to condense into a **protosun** (or pre-sun)

Figure 2.1 Where We are in the Milky Way

Figure 2.1 indicates the location of our Sun and solar system within the Milky Way galaxy. As you can see, the Milky Way is shaped like a flat disc. The bulging center is called the **Galactic Center**, which is thought to contain a great deal of dense matter, called a **black hole**. Four star-filled arms (those are the dense white streaks that encircle the Galactic Center) spiral out from the center. Our solar system is located on an outer arm of the galaxy, about 26,000 light years from the Galactic Center.

FORMATION OF THE SUN AND ASTEROIDS

The protosun, the material that eventually became the Sun, was created by substances that were being pulled toward the center of the disk by gravity. Currents moving away from the center of the disk formed the basis of what would become planets. As the gaseous cloud spun, it collapsed into a dense, hot sphere. As the protosun stabilized, its temperature dropped and iron and nickel solidified from its melted state. Then, silicon, calcium, and other rock-forming minerals solidified. Fragments of these minerals became **asteroids** and then, planets.

FORMATION OF THE TERRESTRIAL PLANETS

Over tens of millions of years, the asteroids collided and joined to form the four inner planets, or **terrestrial planets**. These are Mercury, Venus, Earth and Mars.

As the terrestrial planets consolidated into **protoplanets**, which later became full-fledged official planets, they cleared the inner solar system of material, allowing **solar radiation** to heat the surface of the planets. The terrestrial planets were unable to accumulate lighter gaseous elements and compounds, such as hydrogen, ammonia and methane. These lighter gases were moved out of the inner solar system by **solar winds**, a stream of charged particles radiating from the Sun into space.

FORMATION OF THE OUTER PLANETS

Away from the hot inner solar system, those lighter gases were able to build up. They found a home in the Jovian planets.

The **Jovian planets,** Jupiter, Saturn, Uranus, and Neptune are located much farther from the Sun than the terrestrial planets and are much larger. These four outer planets are composed of water, carbon dioxide, ammonia and methane. These are often called **Gas Giants.**

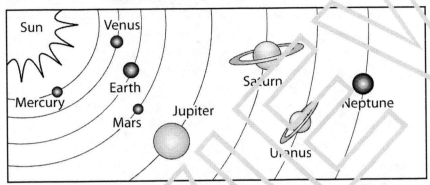

Figure 2.2 The Solar System

A planet's ability to retain an atmosphere depends on its mass and temperature. The Jovian planets have very thick, gaseous atmospheres, in contrast to the much thinner atmospheres of the terrestrial planets.

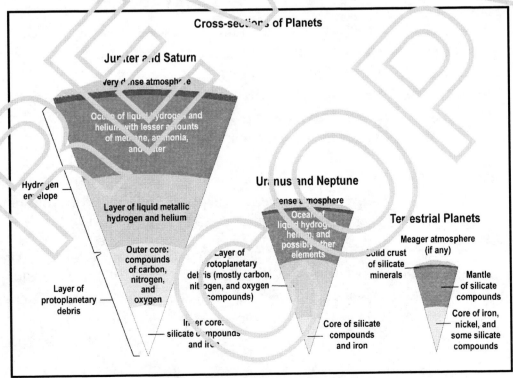

Figure 2.3 Cross-sections of the Planets

The planets can be compared in other ways, too. Table 2.1 will give you an idea of how the eight planets shape up.

Table 2.1

Planet	Solar orbit (days)	Size, as a % of Earth's size	Planet Type	Mean surface temperature	Moons
Mercury	88	38.3	Terrestrial	332° F	0
Venus	224	95	Terrestrial	867° F	0
Earth	365	100	Terrestrial	57° F	1
Mars	687	53.1	Terrestrial	-81° F	2
Jupiter	4333	1120	Gas Giant	-186° F	63
Saturn	10,756	945	Gas Giant	-202° F	56
Uranus	30,707	400	Gas Giant	-337° F	27
Neptune	60,223	388	Gas Giant	-364° F	13

Look at the column in the Table called "Mean Surface Temperature." Do you know what that *means?* The *mean* surface temperature is the *average* temperature at the planet's surface. Since no human has ever been to Jupiter, you may wonder how we can know the temperature there. Well, it is actually calculated. Even though it is far from the Sun, Jupiter still receives solar radiation. It absorbs some of it and reflects some of it. Astronomers can determine how much light (energy) is reflected, by the planet's spectrum. From there they can figure out how much energy is absorbed by the planet, and kept as heat.

On Jupiter, the mean surface temperature is -186°F! That is cold!

On the other hand, the planet with the highest mean surface temperature is Venus. Venus, which is often called Earth's sister planet, is closer to the Sun than Earth, and so it is expected that it would be hotter than Earth. However, if you look closely, you will see that Venus is also considerably hotter than Mercury, the planet closest to the Sun! The reason is that Venus has a very thick atmosphere with a high percentage of the greenhouse gas CO_2 (carbon dioxide). Venus has experienced a runaway **greenhouse effect**, resulting in dramatic **global warming**.

A LEAGUE OF THEIR OWN

Pluto is not included as either a Jovian or terrestrial planet. In fact, the **International Astronomical Union (IAU)** has concluded that Pluto is not a planet at all!

There are several recently discovered objects, referred to either as **minor plantets** or trans-Neptunian objects, that do not have the atmosphere or orbit to be defined as major planets. A **trans-Neptunian object** (TNO) is an astronomical object that orbits the sun at a greater distance than that of the planet Neptune. Pluto is now a TNO, no longer our 9th planet.

Chapter 2 Practice Questions

1. The atmosphere of Jovian planets (Jupiter, Saturn, Uranus, Neptune) is made of

   A. carbon dioxide, oxygen, nitrogen and ammonia.

   B. oxygen, ammonia, ozone and carbon monoxide.

   C. water, carbon dioxide, ammonia and methane.

   D. water, carbon, magnesium and calcium.

2. Neptune is

   A. the eighth planet.

   B. a TNO.

   C. larger than Jupiter.

   D. both A and B.

3. The smallest planet in our solar system is

   A. Mercury.

   B. Mars.

   C. Neptune.

   D. Venus.

4. The planet with the shortest orbit around the sun is

   A. Mercury.

   B. Mars.

   C. Neptune.

   D. Venus.

5. Which of the following statements makes an accurate inference?

   A. "Gas giant" is another name for "Jovian planet."

   B. There is always a direct relationship between a planet's distance from the Sun and its mean surface temperature.

   C. None of the outer four planets has a core.

   D. There is always a direct relationship between a planet's distance from the Sun and its size.

1. Ⓐ	Ⓑ	Ⓒ	Ⓓ
2. Ⓐ	Ⓑ	Ⓒ	Ⓓ
3. Ⓐ	Ⓑ	Ⓒ	Ⓓ
4. Ⓐ	Ⓑ	Ⓒ	Ⓓ
5. Ⓐ	Ⓑ	Ⓒ	Ⓓ

Mini - Review

Look at the following two illustrations. Describe what you see.

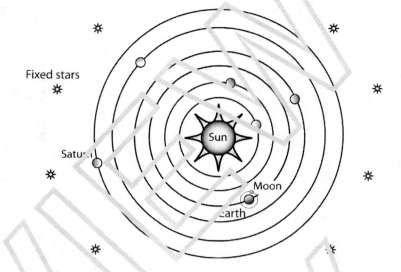

What is wrong with these illustrations?

What theory about the arrangement of our Solar System is described by each?

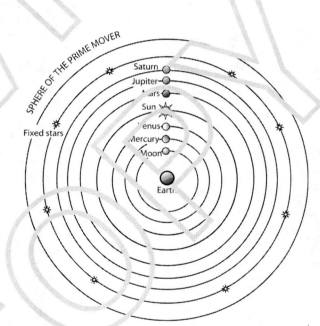

What is missing from each?

Chapter 3
Comets, Asteroids and Meteors

GEORGIA 6TH GRADE CRCT IN SCIENCE STANDARDS COVERED IN THIS CHAPTER INCLUDE:

S6E1f	Describe the characteristics of comets, asteroids, and meteors.

COMETS

Remember what happened to all that protoplanetary debris left over from the formation of our solar system? It was blown away by **solar winds**. Where did it go? Astronomers hypothesize that it blew to the farthest outer reaches of the solar system, where it continues to provide the seed material for **comets**.

Comets are actually minor planets. Their core is called a **nucleus** and is composed of rock, dust and ice. They orbit the Sun in a regular, elliptical (oval) pattern. In cases where they do not orbit regularly, it is usually because the gravitational pull of one of the eight planets has changed their path.

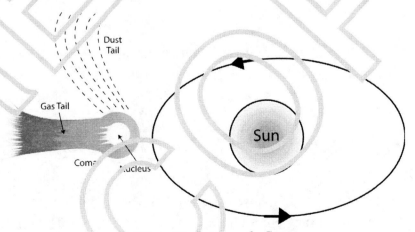

Figure 3.1 Structure of a Comet

The **coma** is a kind of atmosphere that surrounds the comet, composed of ice and dust. The tail of the comet, as shown in Figure 3.1, is actually two tails. One is a dust tail and the other is a gas tail. These two tails point in different directions. The **dust tail** is left behind the comet as it orbits. The **gas tail** always points away from the

Sun, no matter where the comet is in its orbit. That is because the gas tail contains ions which are strongly affected by the charged solar wind. The comet's dust tail is what one sees from Earth as the comet streaks across the sky. The brightness of the tail depends on how close the comet comes to Earth.

The most famous comet is Halley's Comet, which passes by the Earth every 75 – 76 years. It has been recorded throughout man's history on Earth, at least as early as 240 BC. It last came in 1986 and will come again in 2061.

ASTEROIDS

Asteroids are also minor planets, but they are *really* minor. Most asteroids are only a kilometer or so in diameter. By far the largest asteroid is Ceres, with a diameter of 950 km. The next largest asteroids (like 4 Vesta, shown on the left in Figure 3.2) are about 500 km in diameter. Ceres orbits the Sun in an elliptical path that cuts through the asteroid belt. The **asteroid belt** is a region between Mars and Jupiter where asteroids are plentiful.

Figure 3.2 Vesta, Ceres and our Moon (Luna)

Asteroids are also thought to be remnants of protoplanetary debris, but these remnants were not blown into outer space as was the case with comet material. It is thought that the gravitational field of Jupiter prevented this, essentially trapping asteroid material in the asteroid belt.

METEOROIDS

Meteoroids are not minor planets, but rather "space trash." They may be tiny (the size of a dust mote) or large (the size of a riding lawn mower). No matter their size, they are all called **meteoroids** when they are in space. If they enter the Earth's atmosphere they begin to heat up. The burning of the meteoroid produces a tail, which we call a **shooting star**. In actuality, the visible stream of light is, itself, called a meteor. A **meteor** is defined as the visible evidence of the entry of a meteoroid into the atmosphere.

When a comet passes by the Earth, its dust tail leaves behind a trail of debris. All of this space trash falls into the atmosphere at once, creating a **meteor shower**.

MAN-MADE "SPACE TRASH"

Let's think about another kind of meteoroid — the man-made kind. Since the Soviet Union (now Russia) launched the first satellite Sputnick in 1957, there have been more than 4,000 man-made satellites launched into space. All of that space traffic has also created a lot of additional space trash — more than 8,000 man-made objects now orbit the Earth, and many of these are pieces that have fallen off satellites and shuttles. More than 500 of these are large enough to cause damage. For this reason, the National Aeronautics and Space Administration (NASA) tracks them. You can find maps of their location at liftoff.msfc.nass.gov.

Figure 3.2 A Satellite in Orbit

Chapter 3 Practice Questions

1. What part of a comet always points away from the Sun?

   A. the coma   C. the gas tail

   B. the dust tail   D. the nucleus

2. The dust tail of a comet can stretch out for 150 million kilometers. That distance is

   A. more than one light year.

   B. less than one light year.

   C. as wide as the Milky Way.

   D. more than the distance between the Earth and the Sun.

3. What astronomical event often results from the passing of a comet?

   A. a meteor shower

   B. asteroid formation

   C. disruption of a planet's orbit

   D. asteroid belt formation

4. The largest asteroids are

   A. larger than our moon.

   B. smaller than our moon.

   C. about the same size as our moon.

   D. about a kilometer in diameter.

5. In our solar system, most asteroids are found

   A. in a belt between Mars and Earth.

   B. in a belt between Mars and Jupiter.

   C. emerging from the tail of a comet.

   D. stuck in the orbit of Jupiter.

1. Ⓐ Ⓑ Ⓒ Ⓓ
2. Ⓐ Ⓑ Ⓒ Ⓓ
3. Ⓐ Ⓑ Ⓒ Ⓓ
4. Ⓐ Ⓑ Ⓒ Ⓓ
5. Ⓐ Ⓑ Ⓒ Ⓓ

Chapter 4
Rotation and Revolution

GEORGIA 6TH GRADE CRCT IN SCIENCE STANDARDS COVERED IN THIS CHAPTER INCLUDE:

S6E1d	Explain the motion of objects in the day/night sky in terms of relative position.

ROTATION AND REVOLUTION

The Earth rotates (spins) every 24 hours around an imaginary line, an **axis** that runs from the North Pole through the Earth to the South Pole. The rate of rotation is different at different locations on Earth. For instance, at the poles, the rate of rotation is zero. At the equator, the speed of rotation is 1,600 kilometers (1000 miles) per hour.

The Earth revolves in an **orbit** around the Sun at an average distance of 149,000,000 kilometers (93,000,000 miles) from the Sun. Earth travels around the Sun in an **orbital plane**, as if it were moving on a flat sheet of paper. The Earth completes one revolution around the Sun every 365 days, at a speed of 106,000 kilometers (66,000 miles) per hour. The **period** of an orbit is the time it takes for a planet to complete one revolution around the Sun. Thus, for Earth, the period is 365 days, or one year.

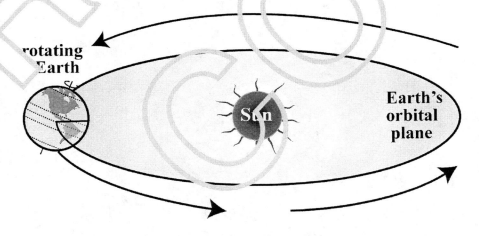

Figure 4.1 Earth's Yearly Orbit

SEASONAL CHANGES

As the Earth rotates around its axis every 24 hours, it also revolves in a fixed orbit around the Sun every 365 days. Earth's axis is inclined, or tilted, at 23½ degrees from the plane of its orbit. Earth's axis always points toward the North Star as the planet revolves around the Sun. If Earth's axis were not inclined, there would be no change of seasons because the Sun's rays would always strike the surface in the same way.

The graphic below illustrates the relationship between the Earth and the Sun throughout the course of one year. As you can see, the Earth's axis always points in the same direction, regardless of where it is in its orbit.

On June 21 or 22, Earth's axis is tilted 23½ degrees toward the Sun, and the vertical rays of the Sun strike the surface at 23½ degrees north of the equator at the latitude line known as the **Tropic of Cancer**. In the Northern Hemisphere, this day is called the **summer solstice** and has the most hours of daylight out of all the days in the year.

Six months later, Earth has traveled through half of its revolution and is opposite of its location on the summer solstice. Earth's axis is now tilted away from the Sun, and the Sun's vertical rays now strike at 23½ degrees of latitude south of the equator at the **Tropic of Capricorn**. In the Northern Hemisphere, this is known as the **winter solstice**, and it occurs on December 21 or 22. The winter solstice is the day with the least amount of daylight in the year.

Midway between the solstices are the **equinoxes.** September 22 or 23 is the **autumnal equinox**, and March 21 or 22 is the **spring equinox**. On these days, the vertical rays of the Sun strike the equator, the latitude that circles the Earth at its widest point. On these days, the amount of daylight is 12 hours in both the Northern and Southern Hemispheres.

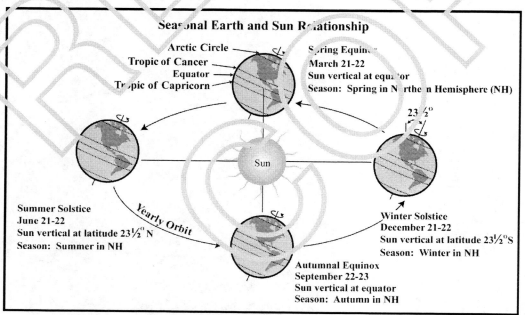

Figure 4.2 Sun/Earth Relationship

Revolution also explains why stars appear in different positions in the sky from month to month. There are some stars that we recognize by themselves, like **Polaris** (the North Star). We may think of other stars as part of a **constellation**, which is a grouping of stars in a certain region of the sky. There are 88 modern constellations, including **Ursa Major**, which is where the **Big Dipper** can be found.

Remember Figure 1.4 in Chapter 1? It showed the blurring of the Big Dipper that will result from the warping of the universe over a long, long period of time — many thousands of years. But from day to day and month to month, the constellations track a much more predictable pattern across the sky. As Earth revolves around the Sun (over the period of a year), the stars appear to move across our night sky. In reality, they are not moving (well, not much anyway), but we are... so our perception of their positions changes.

You can pick up a star chart at the book store, which will show you the constellations that can be seen in the sky at different times of the year. There are also magazines and websites that will do the same. Figure 4.3 below indicates the approximate months that each constellation of the **zodiac** is most visible. (The 12 constellations of the zodiac are some of the most well-known in popular culture). As an example, Taurus is most clearly viewed in December.

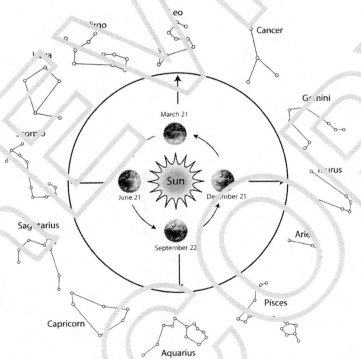

Figure 4.3 The Zodiacal Constellations Throughout the Year

Chapter 4 Practice Questions

1. When the Earth's axis is tilted away from the Sun in the Northern Hemisphere, the season there is

    A. summer.

    B. winter.

    C. spring.

    D. fall.

2. The Earth _____ on its axis one time every 24 hours, producing day and night.

    A. revolves

    B. rotates

    C. rejuvenates

    D. changes orbit

3. The Earth _____ around the Sun one time every 365 days.

    A. revolves

    B. rotates

    C. rejuvenates

    D. changes orbit

4. A constellation is

    A. one of the 12 regions of the sky.

    B. one of the 88 regions of the sky.

    C. the brightest star in the sky.

    D. the same as the zodiac.

5. Which of the following contains the longest day of the year?

    A. spring equinox

    B. summer solstice

    C. autumnal equinox

    D. winter solstice

1. Ⓐ Ⓑ Ⓒ Ⓓ
2. Ⓐ Ⓑ Ⓒ Ⓓ
3. Ⓐ Ⓑ Ⓒ Ⓓ
4. Ⓐ Ⓑ Ⓒ Ⓓ
5. Ⓐ Ⓑ Ⓒ Ⓓ

Chapter 5
Gravity and Orbit

S6E1e	Explain that gravity is one force that governs the motion in the solar system.

In the last chapter, we discussed the difference between rotation and revolution. As you now know, the path traced the revolution of a planet, comet, asteroid or meteoroid around the Sun is called an **orbit**. More generally, the orbit is the path that an object takes around another object. The reason for the orbit is that both objects have a **gravitational attraction** for one another.

Gravity is a force that attracts objects to one another. Every object has gravity, but the greater the mass of the object, the more gravity it has. **Mass** is a measure of how much matter an object contains. Loosely speaking, it describes how heavy the object is. For instance, the U.S. nickel coin is made up of copper and nickel. The mass of that matter is about 5 grams

Mass = 5 grams

Figure 5.1

The Sun has a mass of about 1.99×10^{31} kilograms, so it exerts a great deal of gravitational force. In fact, the Sun has enough gravitational force to attract our entire solar system toward it.

So why don't the planets become so attracted that they simply fall into the Sun? Well, to put it simply, because they are already moving. This is **Newton's First Law of Motion**, and it can be stated as follows:

> **A moving object will continue to move in the same direction, with the same speed, unless some outside force acts to change its motion.**

The tendency of an object to continue moving in the same way that it has been moving is called **inertia**, so Newton's First Law is sometimes call the **law of inertia**. The planets are moving in a certain direction, at a certain speed, until something changes that motion. The "something" that affects their motion is the force called gravity. The orbit of a planet is the result of the inertial movement of a huge object (a planet), balanced by the gravitational pull of an even bigger object (the Sun).

The shape of the orbital path is not circular, but **elliptical** — that is, it is oval. The exact *oval-ness* of the orbit is different for every planet. If you think about it, the oval can look like either of the following, or anywhere in between.

Figure 5.2 Elliptical Orbit Shapes

If the planet has a very flat oval orbit, the orbit is said to be **very eccentric**. Mercury has the most eccentric orbit of the eight planets. (Though before Pluto was removed from our list of official planets, it had the most eccentric orbit) If the planet has a more rounded orbit, it is said to be **less eccentric**. Venus and Neptune have the least eccentric orbits.

Sometimes the shape of a planet's orbital path changes a little, becoming more or less eccentric. This happens when the forces (gravity and inertia) become unbalanced. More specifically, when one planet falls under the influence of another planet's gravitational pull, their orbit around the Sun is altered. The force of gravity is greatly affected by distance, so, closer objects pull more than objects that are far away. In the end, though, the Sun has a far greater mass than any planet, and its gravity pulls the planet back into its usual orbital path.

Chapter 5 Practice Questions

1. An ellipse can best be described as

   A. a circle.

   B. an oval.

   C. a rhombus.

   D. a cone.

2. Marble X is rolled across the concrete and strikes the motionless Marble Y. Which of the following statements best describes the result?

   A. Marble X and Marble Y both have inertia, which changes when they collide.

   B. Only Marble X has inertia.

   C. Only Marble Y has inertia.

   D. Neither marble has inertia, but their gravity pulls them into contact.

3. Which planet has the most eccentric orbit?

   A. Venus

   B. Earth

   C. Mercury

   D. Neptune

4. The inertial force of the Earth

   A. acts in a different direction than the gravitational force of the Sun.

   B. acts in the same direction as the gravitational force of the Sun.

   C. acts in the same direction as the inertial force of the other planets.

   D. acts in the opposite direction as the inertial force of the other planets.

5. Gravitational force

   A. pulls a planet toward another planet.

   B. pulls a planet toward the Sun.

   C. keeps a planet moving in the same direction as it was moving.

   D. pulls a planet toward the Sun and other planets.

1. Ⓐ Ⓑ Ⓒ Ⓓ
2. Ⓐ Ⓑ Ⓒ Ⓓ
3. Ⓐ Ⓑ Ⓒ Ⓓ
4. Ⓐ Ⓑ Ⓒ Ⓓ
5. Ⓐ Ⓑ Ⓒ Ⓓ

Mini - Review

Describe the diagram. Use the following questions to help guide your discussion.

What kind of celestial ojbect is pictured here?

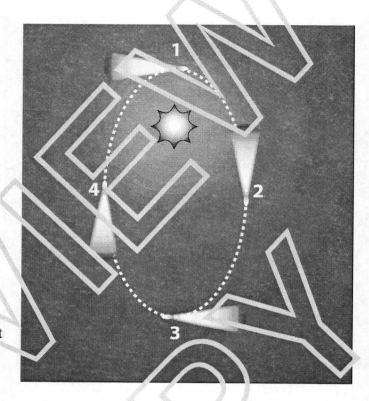

What is the shape of its orbit?

What holds it in orbit?

Describe the cone of debris at its end and what it will cause.

Chapter 6
The Phases of the Moon

GEORGIA 6TH GRADE CRCT IN SCIENCE STANDARDS COVERED IN THIS CHAPTER INCLUDE:

S6E2a	Demonstrate the phases of the Moon by showing the alignment of the Earth, Moon, and Sun.

THE MOON

One of the biggest misconceptions about the Moon is that its phases are caused by the Earth's shadow. The Earth's shadow causes eclipses, but it has nothing to do with phases. Rather, the phases of the Moon are produced by the alignment of the Moon and the Sun in the sky.

The position of the Sun and Moon determines the **phase of the Moon**. At new moon, the angle between the Sun and Moon is small, less than a few degrees. At first quarter, when the Moon is half full, the Moon lies 90 degrees east of the Sun. For example, if you were to point to the setting Sun with one arm and to the Moon with the other, the angle between your arms would be 90 degrees. At full, the Moon is 180 degrees from the Sun. At last quarter, it is 90 degrees west of the Sun. On its journey from new moon to full moon, it is said to be **waxing** (increasing). As it proceeds from full moon to dark moon, it is **waning** (decreasing). Table 6.1 and Figure 6.1 describe these phases.

Table 6.1 Phases of the Moon

Position	1	2	3	4	5	6	7	8
Phase	new	waxing crescent	first quarter	waxing gibbous	full	waning gibbous	third quarter	waning crescent
Visibility	tiny crescent	increasing crescent	half moon	increasing toward full	full	decreasing toward half	half moon	decreasing to dark moon

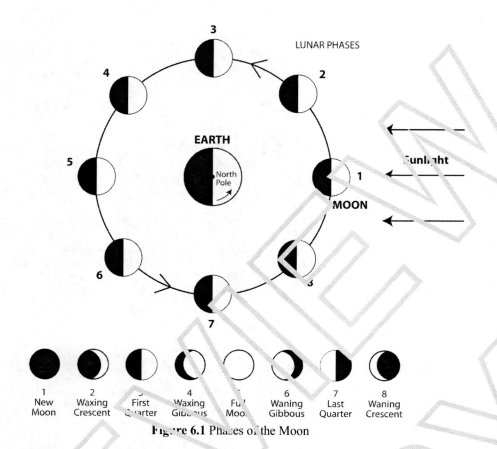

Figure 6.1 Phases of the Moon

The new moon is essentially invisible because it is between the Earth and the Sun and therefore lost in the glare of the Sun. Even on day 2 or 3, it is tough to spot the Moon because it is just the tiniest sliver and still close to the Sun. The waxing crescent moon grows until it is about half full in the phase we call first quarter. From there it grows to full moon and then begins to shrink back to last quarter, waning crescent and finally back to new moon.

The first and last quarter moons mark the halfway points between the new moon and full moon. The first quarter moon is illuminated on the right hand side. The last quarter moon is illuminated on the left hand side. It might seem weird to call a half full moon first or last quarter, but the quarter refers to the *position* of the Moon in the sky, *not its phase.* A quarter moon is one quarter of a full circle (90°) away from the Sun.

The lighted part of the Moon always points the way to the Sun. This means that a waxing crescent moon in the western sky at sunset has the lighted part on the right which is the direction of the sun. The sequence of the lunar phases always proceeds with the lighted part of the Moon growing from right to left until the Moon reaches full. After full moon, the light recedes from right to left until new moon.

There is about a week between each major phase of the Lunar Cycle — that is, 7 – 8 days between new moon and first quarter, between first quarter and full and so on.

Chapter 6 Practice Questions

1. A gibbous moon is

   A. bigger than a half moon.

   B. bigger than a half moon, but less than a full moon.

   C. smaller than a half moon.

   D. a dark moon.

2. Which percentage best describes the visibility of a waxing crescent moon? (Hint: a full moon is 100% visible.)

   A. 0%

   B. 1% – 49%

   C. 50%

   D. 51% – 99%

3. The Moon in its second quarter is

   A. full.

   B. waxing.

   C. waning.

   D. new.

4. A waxing moon is

   A. proceeding from new to full.

   B. proceeding from full to new.

   C. nearly dark.

   D. in positions 5 – 8.

5. The phases of the Moon are caused by the

   A. Earth's shadow.

   B. Sun's shadow.

   C. orientation of the Sun and the Moon.

   D. orientation of the Sun and the Earth.

Mini - Review

There are 8 phases of the Moon. Without looking, draw a diagram that shows what each phase looks like.

Chapter 7
Lunar and Solar Eclipses

GEORGIA 6TH GRADE CRCT IN SCIENCE STANDARDS COVERED IN THIS CHAPTER INCLUDE:

S6E2b	Explain the alignment of the Earth, Moon and Sun during solar and lunar eclipses.

You know from the last chapter that the Earth revolves around the Sun, and the Moon revolves around the Earth. The overall arrangement is shown in Figure 7.1. Although the drawing is not to scale, you can see that the Earth is much larger than the Moon, and the Sun is much larger than the Earth. (But you knew that already, didn't you?)

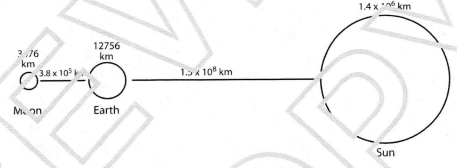

Figure 7.1 Position of the Earth, Moon and Sun

This arrangement has some interesting consequences, namely eclipses! An **eclipse** is an astronomical event that occurs when one object moves into the shadow of another.

ECLIPSES

Because the Moon orbits the Earth at an angle, approximately +/– 5° relative to the Earth-Sun plane, the Moon crosses the Earth's orbital plane only twice a year. These times are called **eclipse seasons**, because they are the only times when eclipses can occur.

For an eclipse to take place, the Moon must be in the correct phase during an eclipse season; for a solar eclipse, it must be a **new moon**, and for a lunar eclipse it must be a **full moon**. This condition makes solar eclipses relatively rare and hard to spot.

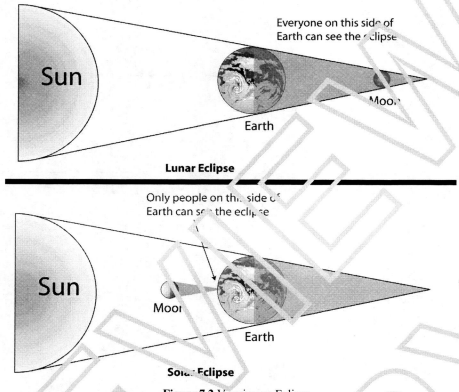

Figure 7.2 Viewing an Eclipse

SCEF (SOME COOL ECLIPSE FACTS)

- A solar eclipse always occurs two weeks before or after a lunar eclipse.
- Eclipses very often occur in threes, alternating lunar – solar – lunar.
- The maximum time a lunar eclipse can last is 3 hours and 40 minutes.
- The longest time the Moon can stay in total eclipse is 1 hour 40 minutes.
- The maximum time for a total solar eclipse is 7 minutes and 40 seconds.
- The maximum time for an partial solar eclipse is 12 minutes 24 seconds.
- Lunar eclipses are visible over an entire hemisphere.
- Solar eclipses are visible in a narrow path a maximum of 167 miles wide (269km).
- At any geographic position on the Earth, a total solar eclipse occurs an average of once every 360 years.
- The cycle of eclipses repeats every 18.6 years.
- The eclipse shadow moves at 2,000 mph at the Earth's poles and 1,000 mph at the Earth's equator.

Chapter 7 Practice Questions

1. Solar eclipses only occur during

   A. winter.

   B. a new moon.

   C. a full moon.

   D. spring.

2. The orbit of the Earth around the Sun occurs in a plane, which you can visualize as a flat disc. The Moon orbits the Earth at an angle to that plane, which is

   A. $+5°$

   B. $-5°$

   C. $+10°$

   D. $+/- 5°$

3. Which of the following events is the most common?

   A. partial lunar eclipse

   B. total lunar eclipse

   C. partial solar eclipse

   D. total solar eclipse

4. Lunar eclipses can be seen by

   A. only those in a small area.

   B. one hemisphere of the Earth.

   C. both hemispheres of the Earth.

   D. only those in the Western Hemisphere.

5. Solar eclipses are only visible to a small portion of the Earth because

   A. the shadow cast by the Moon is large.

   B. the shadow cast by the Moon is small.

   C. the Sun shines less strongly when the Moon is in front of it.

   D. the shadow cast by the Sun is large.

1. (A) (B) (C) (D)
2. (A) (B) (C) (D)
3. (A) (B) (C) (D)
4. (A) (B) (C) (D)
5. (A) (B) (C) (D)

Chapter 8
The Tilt of the Earth

GEORGIA 6TH GRADE CRCT IN SCIENCE STANDARDS COVERED IN THIS CHAPTER INCLUDE:

S6E2c	Relate the tilt of the Earth to the distribution of sunlight throughout the year and its effect on climate.

The position and motion of the Earth in space seem like two things that are very far away from our everyday life. But they are important to our life here on Earth. The rotation and revolution of the Earth govern our days, nights, time and calendar. They also determine our seasons. In order to see how, let's look back to the relationship between the Sun and the Earth.

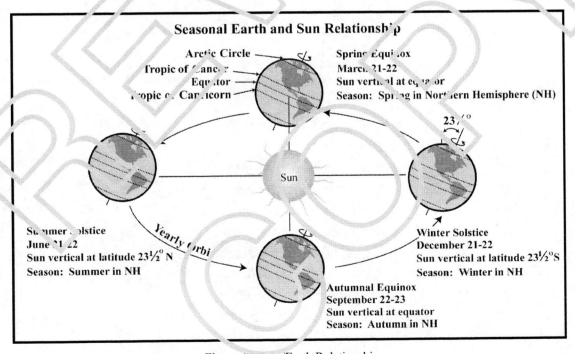

Figure 8.1 Sun/Earth Relationship

As the Earth revolves (orbits) around the Sun, its position relative to the Sun varies. Earth's position determines the angle at which the Sun's rays strike its surface. As the Earth's position changes, the angle of the Sun's rays striking the Earth also changes. The changing angles of the Sun's rays due to the planet's position are one of the factors determining the change in seasons.

The angle of the Earth in relation to the Sun affects the amount of solar energy that reaches the Earth's surface in two ways. The amounts of energy received at different areas of the Earth explain why the Earth is always warmest at the equator and coolest at the poles.

The Sun's rays are more concentrated where they hit at a high angle (90°). Where they hit at a lower angle (30°), the rays are less concentrated. One unit of solar energy striking the Earth at a thirty degree angle covers twice as much land area (and is consequently less intense) as one unit of solar energy striking the Earth at a ninety degree angle.

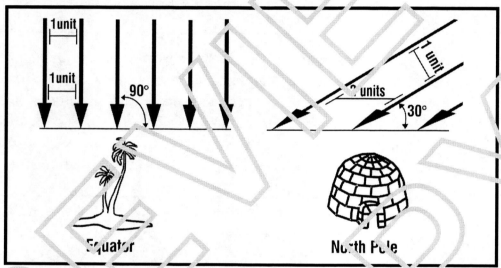

Figure 8.2 Angle of the Sun's Radiation

A less important consideration that determines the amount of energy reaching Earth's surface is the amount of atmosphere that the Sun's rays must travel through. This thickness of the atmosphere is also determined by the angle of the Sun. Think of it this way; the more direct the rays, the more energy they carry. Rays striking at the equator are perpendicular and travel through less atmosphere than rays striking at lower angles. Because the rays travel a greater distance through the atmosphere, more of the rays are absorbed, reflected, or scattered by the atmosphere. This absorption, reflection and scattering of rays decreases the intensity of the Sun's rays and the energy they bring to the surface of Earth.

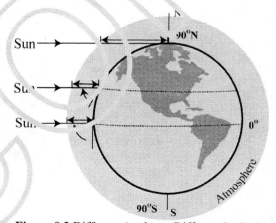

Figure 8.3 Different Angles at Different Latitudes

THE DRIVING FORCE

Energy from the Sun is generated by a process called **nuclear fusion**, and this energy is called **solar radiation**. Solar radiation moves through space at the speed of light 300,000 kilometers per second (kps) or 3.0×10^8 m/s. Solar radiation does not need a medium to travel through, so it can travel through space. Solar radiation travels in the form of **electromagnetic waves**, a form of energy wave that moves at the speed of light. The Sun produces many types of electromagnetic waves, some of which pass easily through the atmosphere and reach the Earth's surface. These include mostly visible light, infrared rays and a little ultraviolet light. Other waves are absorbed more strongly by the atmosphere, and do not reach the Earth's surface.

Electromagnetic waves produced by the Sun provide energy that is converted to heat once they reach an object like the Earth. These waves do not heat space or the air surrounding the Earth to any great degree, but they travel through space and the Earth's atmosphere until they strike an object. When the waves reach an object, the energy in the waves is converted to heat. The heated object can be a plant, an animal or the Earth itself. For example, if you sit outside in the Sun on a cool day, you will probably still feel warm in spite of the temperature because the electromagnetic waves from the Sun heat your body. If a cloud comes by and blocks the Sun, the Sun's electromagnetic waves from the Sun are also blocked. You will then feel chilly since the Sun's energy that is giving you warmth has been blocked. But Beware! The cloud does not block out the ultraviolet rays that burn your skin and cause cancer. So keep that sunscreen on!

Chapter 8 Practice Questions

1. During an equinox, solar radiation striking the Earth at the equator is

   A. weaker than solar radiation that strikes at higher latitudes.

   B. weaker than solar radiation that strikes at lower latitudes.

   C. stronger than solar radiation striking at any other latitude.

   D. reflected more dramatically than solar radiation striking at any other latitude.

2. The Earth is

   A. warmest at the poles.

   B. warmest at the equator.

   C. warmest in June.

   D. warmest in August.

3. Alaska is colder than Florida because

   A. the Sun's rays strike at a higher angle in Florida than Alaska.

   B. the Sun's rays strike at a lower angle in Florida than Alaska.

   C. the thinner atmosphere at the poles absorbs more solar radiation.

   D. the thinner atmosphere at the equator scatters more solar radiation.

4. The equator is found at a latitude of

   A. 90°.   C. 23 ½ N.

   B. 23 ½° S.   D. 0.°

5. Solar radiation is

   A. made up of only visible, infrared and ultraviolet radiation.

   B. almost entirely absorbed by the atmosphere.

   C. transferred as heat to solids and liquids on Earth.

   D. travels at 300,000 meters per second.

1. (A) (B) (C) (D)
2. (A) (B) (C) (D)
3. (A) (B) (C) (D)
4. (A) (B) (C) (D)
5. (A) (B) (C) (D)

Domain One Review

Choose the best answer for each Review question. Bubble in your answers in the space provided on the answer sheet below.

1. Ⓐ Ⓑ Ⓒ Ⓓ   11. Ⓐ Ⓑ Ⓒ Ⓓ
2. Ⓐ Ⓑ Ⓒ Ⓓ   12. Ⓐ Ⓑ Ⓒ Ⓓ
3. Ⓐ Ⓑ Ⓒ Ⓓ   13. Ⓐ Ⓑ Ⓒ Ⓓ
4. Ⓐ Ⓑ Ⓒ Ⓓ   14. Ⓐ Ⓑ Ⓒ Ⓓ
5. Ⓐ Ⓑ Ⓒ Ⓓ   15. Ⓐ Ⓑ Ⓒ Ⓓ
6. Ⓐ Ⓑ Ⓒ Ⓓ   16. Ⓐ Ⓑ Ⓒ Ⓓ
7. Ⓐ Ⓑ Ⓒ Ⓓ   17. Ⓐ Ⓑ Ⓒ Ⓓ
8. Ⓐ Ⓑ Ⓒ Ⓓ   18. Ⓐ Ⓑ Ⓒ Ⓓ
9. Ⓐ Ⓑ Ⓒ Ⓓ   19. Ⓐ Ⓑ Ⓒ Ⓓ
10. Ⓐ Ⓑ Ⓒ Ⓓ   20. Ⓐ Ⓑ Ⓒ Ⓓ

Use the following diagram to answer question 1.

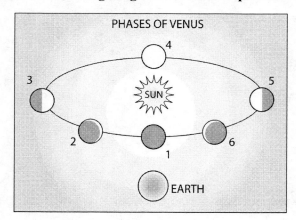

PHASES OF VENUS

1. Galileo discovered in the early 17th century that Venus had phases like our moon. Venus is new at position 1 and full at position 4. In one phase is it impossible to see Venus from Earth because no light is reflected. Which phase is it?

   A. phase 1   C. phase 4

   B. phase 3   D. phase 5

2. As the Moon moves through its phases, its appearance in our sky changes. During which of the following phase changes is the Moon waxing?

   A. first quarter to full

   B. full to third quarter

   C. third quarter to new

   D. none of these

3. The Big Bang explains

   A. how the universe was formed

   B. how the Milky Way was formed.

   C. how the Big Dipper was formed.

   D. how planets orbit around the Sun.

4. Which of the following would be most likely to alter the orbital path of Earth?

   A. Halley's comet approaches Earth

   B. Earth's orbit approaches Mars

   C. Earth's orbit approaches Venus

   D. A meteor shower

5. Which planet has the longest orbit around the Sun?

   A. Mercury   C. Jupiter

   B. Neptune   D. Uranus

6. What is the hottest planet in our Solar system?

   A. Mercury   C. Venus

   B. Mars   D. Saturn

7. Alpha Centauri is the closest star system to our own Solar system. It is about 4.4 light years away from Earth. That distance is

   A. greater than the diameter of the Milky Way.

   B. less than 10 trillion kilometers away.

   C. more than 50 trillion kilometers away.

   D. between 10 and 50 trillion kilometers away.

8. Which of the following is a trans-Neptunian object (TNO)?

   A. Ceres   C. Pluto

   B. Luna   D. Neptune

9. Solstices occur in

   A. winter and summer.

   B. autumn and spring.

   C. winter and autumn.

   D. summer and spring.

10. A meteor shower is commonly seen on Earth after

A. Earth crosses through the asteroid belt.

B. a comet passes.

C. an asteroid passes.

D. a solar eclipse.

11. If the Moon revolved around the Earth twice as quickly as it does now, what would be the most direct effect?

A. shorter months

B. shorter days

C. shorter years

D. shorter seasons

12. Which of the following has the thickest atmosphere?

A. Mars

B. Mercury

C. Venus

D. Earth

13. Which planet(s) in our Solar system have a noticeable ring structure?

A. Saturn

B. Saturn and Uranus

C. Saturn and Neptune

D. Saturn and Jupiter

14. When Halley's Comet passes by Earth, we can see it in the sky for a few weeks. What main feature of the comet do we see?

A. the coma

B. the nucleus

C. the dust tail

D. the gas tail

15. Saturn's rings range from 6,600-120,000 kilometers away from the planet. Saturn's closest moon is Mimas, which orbits at a distance of 185,000 kilometers. Mimas is

A. orbiting within the rings of the planet.

B. orbiting the planet inside the rings.

C. orbiting the planet outside the rings.

D. almost two light years from Saturn.

16. In general, Gas Giants

A. have more moons than terrestrial planets.

B. are hotter than terrestrial planets.

C. have thinner atmospheres than terrestrial planets.

D. have shorter orbits than terrestrial planets.

17. The Northern Hemisphere contains the United States. What else can be found in the Northern Hemisphere?

A. the Tropic of Capricorn

B. the Tropic of Cancer

C. the Equator

D. Antarctica

18. There are 111 elements on the Periodic Table. The Big Bang theory explains that all existing elements were initially formed from the

A. fusion of hydrogen atoms.

B. fusion of helium atoms.

C. burning of oxygen atoms.

D. burning of carbon atoms.

19. How does the temperature compare in areas where solar radiation hits the Earth at a 45° angle, versus where the radiation hits the Earth at an 80° angle?

   A. It is hotter where solar radiation hits the Earth at 45°.

   B. It is colder where solar radiation hits the Earth at 45°.

   C. It is always winter where solar radiation hits the Earth at 45°.

   D. It is always winter where solar radiation hits the Earth at 80°.

20. Which of the following is true of a solar eclipse?

   A. Solar eclipses can be seen by people all over the Earth.

   B. Solar eclipses are shorter in duration than lunar eclipses.

   C. Solar eclipses only occur during the full moon.

   D. Solar eclipses are generally more common than lunar eclipses.

Domain Two
Hydrology and Meteorology

DOMAIN TWO COVERS:

Chapter 9 – Bodies of Water

Chapter 10 – The Ocean Floor

Chapter 11 – Ocean Movement I: Tides

Chapter 12 – Ocean Movement II: Waves and Currents

Chapter 13 – Weather Patterns and Events

Chapter 9
Bodies of Water

GEORGIA 6TH GRADE CRCT IN SCIENCE STANDARDS COVERED IN THIS CHAPTER INCLUDE:

S6E3a	Explain that a large portion of the Earth's surface is water, consisting of oceans, rivers, lakes, underground water, and ice.
S6E3b	Relate various atmospheric conditions to stages of the water cycle.
S6E3c	Describe the composition, location, and subsurface topography of the world's oceans.

FOUR EARTHS

Sometimes scientists look at the Earth in the same way a doctor looks at the human body: as a series of systems. In the human body, doctors know how the circulatory system works with the respiratory system, and so on. When scientists look at the Earth this way, they divide the Earth up into four systems (which they call spheres): the **atmosphere**, the **hydrosphere**, the **biosphere** and the **lithosphere**.

- The **atmosphere** is a mixture of gases and suspended particles surrounding the earth. These layers are responsible for Earth's **weather** and for protecting us from harmful rays of the sun.

- All water environments found on Earth make up the **hydrosphere**, including the oceans and all water found above and below the ground. The hydrosphere also includes any water in the atmosphere.

- The **biosphere** includes all living things, both plant and animal.

- The **lithosphere** consists of the Earth's crust, which is the solid, inorganic part of the Earth.

In this chapter, we will focus on the hydrosphere.

The water on Earth is divided into categories, based on its **salinity** — that is, its salt content. **Salt water** areas have a high salinity, about 35 grams of salt per kilogram of water. Areas with **fresh water** have a low salinity; these areas still have salt in the water, but the concentration is very low, less than 1 gram of salt per kilogram of water.

As you will learn in chemistry class, though, there are a lot of different kinds of salt. Salinity is a measure of all of those salts put together. That includes potassium chloride (KCl), magnesium cloride (MgCl) and a great many others. However, most of the ocean's salt is simple table salt — sodium chloride (NaCl).

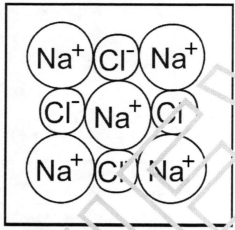

Figure 9.1 Sodium Chloride (NaCl)

Salinity is sometimes indicated as a percentage. So, the percent salinity of the ocean could be reported as 3.5%. This is how it is worked out:

$$\frac{35 \; grams \; salt}{1000 \; milliliters \; water} \cong \frac{35 \; grams \; salt}{1000 \; grams \; water} = \mathbf{0.035} \times 100 = 3.5\%$$

Let's look at where all that salt water can be found.

SALT WATER

The vast majority of water on Earth is salt water, and it can be found in the world's **oceans**. Oceans cover 71% of the Earth's surface. When pictures of the Earth are taken from space, the oceans are the reason why most of the planet appears to be blue. Figure 9.2 shows the world's oceans. There are no distinct physical boundaries between the bodies of water; they are actually all one ocean, called the **World Ocean**. In practice, however, the World Ocean is usually divided

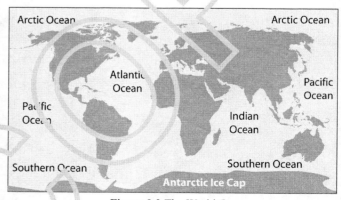

Figure 9.2 The World Ocean

into five individual oceans. By far, the largest is the Pacific Ocean, with a total area of 165 million km^2. Next are the Atlantic Ocean, with 82 million km^2, and the Indian Ocean, with 73 million km^2. Closer to the poles are the smaller, and less frequently navigated Southern and Arctic Oceans, with areas of 20 million and 5 million km², respectively. Some classify the Southern and Arctic Oceans as regions of the Pacific or Atlantic Oceans, but most oceanographers agree that their currents mark them as distinct oceanic regions.

You might be surprised to know that the word "sea" does not mean the same thing as the word "ocean." A **sea** is actually a subdivision of the ocean. Like oceans, seas do not have distinct boundaries, though their approximate boundaries are often well recognized. As shown in Figure 9.3, a sea may either be a general region of open ocean or a distinct region of landlocked salt water. A landlocked sea is the same as a **gulf**.

Figure 9.3 Ocean, Sea and Gulf

FRESH WATER

About 3% the Earth's surface is fresh water. Bodies of water such as glaciers, lakes and rivers are fresh water. **Glaciers** are slow-moving rivers of frozen ice; they are the largest source of fresh water on the planet. A **lake** is a freshwater body of water surrounded on all sides by land. A **river** is a natural waterway that comes from a source (frozen mountaintops, a lake, etc) and flows downhill, usually into an ocean, gulf or sea.

Figure 9.4 River

The fresh water system of Georgia includes many lakes and rivers, as it is shown in Figure 9.5.

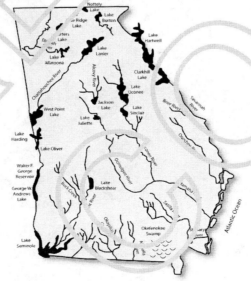

Figure 9.5 Georgia Freshwater Ecosystem

Somewhere in between fresh and salt water is **brackish** water. This can be found in an estuary. An **estuary** is the area where a river empties into an ocean. The water composition here is a mixture of fresh and salt water. The percentage of each is defined by the outward flow of the river and by the tides of the ocean.

Figure 9.6 Estuarial Area

THE WATER CYCLE

Fresh water is vital for all living things. Without it, living cells become dehydrated and the organism dies. With so much salt water on Earth, there must be some mechanism for recycling the small amount of fresh water that exists. And there is: the Water Cycle!

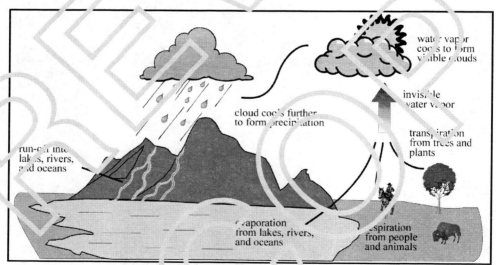

water vapor cools to form visible clouds

invisible water vapor

transpiration from trees and plants

cloud cools further to form precipitation

run-off into lakes, rivers, and oceans

evaporation from lakes, rivers, and oceans

respiration from people and animals

Figure 9.7 The Water Cycle

How does the water cycle work? Precipitation in the form of rain, ice, hail or dew falls to the earth. There it soaks into the ground, runs off of rocks and structures, or accumulates in bodies of water. The Sun provides energy in the form of heat, which drives evaporation. The process of evaporation removes water from the earth, drying the ground, rocks and structures, and lowering the level of bodies of water. In fact, small bodies of water, like puddles and rivulets, usually disappear entirely! Respiration from people and transpiration (which is the release of water from living structures through pores or membranes) from plants also send water into the atmosphere.

No longer Earth-bound, the released water vapor rises into the atmosphere. As it rises, it cools. When it cools, it begins to condense into clouds which eventually become saturated with (full of) water. At that point, the water is released from the clouds as precipitation, which starts the cycle all over again. Without this cycle of precipitation, runoff, and evaporation, a fresh water supply would not be available. Without fresh water you'd run out of energy in a hurry.

Chapter 9 Practice Questions

1. How do clouds release water?

    A. as precipitation

    B. as evaporation

    C. as transpiration

    D. as respiration

2. The smallest ocean is the

    A. Southern Ocean.

    B. Atlantic Ocean

    C. Arctic Ocean.

    D. Indian Ocean.

3. A sea can be which of the following?

    A. almost completely landlocked

    B. a division of open ocean

    C. fresh water

    D. A and B only

4. Transpiration is the release of

    A. water from decaying matter.

    B. water from living organisms.

    C. carbon dioxide from living organisms.

    D. carbon dioxide from plants.

5. The Southern Ocean is isolated in which hemisphere?

    A. southern

    B. northern

    C. eastern

    D. western

1. (A) (B) (C) (D)
2. (A) (B) (C) (D)
3. (A) (B) (C) (D)
4. (A) (B) (C) (D)
5. (A) (B) (C) (D)

Chapter 10
The Ocean Floor

GEORGIA 6TH GRADE CRCT IN SCIENCE STANDARDS COVERED IN THIS CHAPTER INCLUDE:

S6E3c	Describe the composition, location, and subsurface topography of the world's oceans.

Most people living in the interior of the United States are much more familiar with their local fresh water ponds and creeks than they are with the ocean. It doesn't seem that there could be *so much less* fresh water than salt water. The main reason is that the salt water areas, like oceans and seas, are very deep, whereas fresh water sources are usually more shallow. Looking at the deepest underwater features of the ocean requires special equipment.

Submersible vehicles have been built that can withstand great pressures. These can go into very deep areas of the ocean, and they have provided actual photographs. Submersibles allow us to see what life on the ocean floor looks like.

Bathymetry (the study of the depth contours of the ocean floor) allows us to image the ocean floor in a different way, though. A bathymetric map is a map of the ocean floor. This sort of image is much more useful for submarines trying to navigate a given area of ocean. These maps are generated by sonar (**SO**und **N**avigation **A**nd **R**anging). Here is how it works.

A ship or submarine uses an underwater **speaker** to send out a pulse of sound, called a "**ping**." The sonar operator then listens to a **receiver**, and notes the time it takes for the sound to be reflected back to the ship. The speed of sound in water is about 1520 meters per second. If the sonar operator measures 4 seconds from the time the ping is sent, to the time that it returns to the receiver, then he can calculate the distance that the ping has travelled. The equations are.

$$ping\ time \times 1520\ m/s = total\ meters\ travelled$$

$$\frac{total\ meters\ travelled}{2} = distance\ between\ the\ ship\ and\ the\ ocean\ floor$$

Plugging in our data, a 4-second ping translates to an ocean depth of 3040 meters.

Figure 10.1 should help you see how this works.

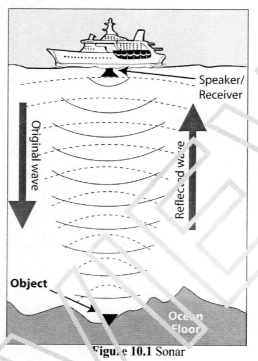

Figure 10.1 Sonar

Oceanographers are scientists who focus their studies on the ocean. They may work with marine plants and animals, water chemistry or current patterns. Many oceanographers examine ocean floor features to learn more about the **oceanic crust** and **plate tectonics** (which we will study more closely in Domain 3). Many regions of the ocean floor have been mapped using bathymetric analysis, helping oceanographers understand the landscape of that hidden part of the

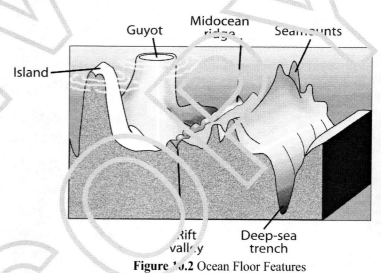

Figure 10.2 Ocean Floor Features

Earth's crust. Figure 10.2 shows a few common geological features of the ocean floor.

OCEANIC TRENCHES

A long, narrow slice into the ocean floor is an ocean trench. Trenches occur at the boundary between two tectonic plates and are the deepest parts of the ocean. As shown in Figure 10.3, the Puerto Rico trench is 800 km long and, at over 8,600 meters deep, the deepest part of the Atlantic Ocean. The Marianas trench in the Pacific Ocean is the deepest known place in any ocean, at nearly 11,000 meters below sea level.

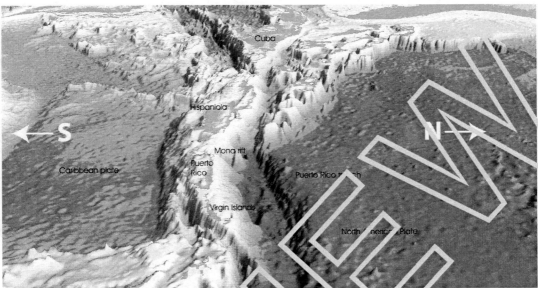

Figure 10.3 Atlantic Ocean Bathymetry at Plate Boundary

SEAMOUNTS AND MID-OCEAN RIDGES

Underwater mountains that do not reach the surface are called **seamounts**. Seamounts that do reach the surface are called **islands**. Flat-topped seamounts, which may once have been volcanoes, are called **guyots**.

Seamounts sometimes occur individually, but seamount ranges are also common. These ranges occur at tectonic plate boundaries and are called **mid-ocean ridges**. Mid-ocean ridges are found in every ocean, and are, in fact, connected to one another. Together, they form the largest mountain range in the world. Figure 10.3 above shows the mid-ocean ridge submerged to the north of Cuba.

RIFT VALLEYS

Rift valleys are deep valleys between the peaks of a mid-ocean ridge system. The rift valley is a natural result of the formation of the ridges. Figure 10.3 shows the Mona rift, located east of the Puerto Rico trench.

As you can see, trenches, seamounts, mid-ocean ridges and rift valleys are all found on the ocean floor. They all result from some kind of tectonic plate activity, which will be explained more clearly as we examine plate tectonics in Domain 2. These features are often associated with underwater **volcanoes** and **hydrothermal vents**, both of which release the heat that results from the movement of tectonic plates against each other. The superheated water emerging from volcanoes and vents is home to some very exotic marine life.

Chapter 10 Practice Questions

1. A ship on the Pacific Ocean pings a section of ocean floor. The ping takes 12 seconds to return. What sort of ocean floor feature has this oceanographer probably located?

   A. a guyot

   B. a trench

   C. a rift valley

   D. a mid-ocean ridge

2. The ship from question #1 pings the ocean floor again, about a kilometer away from the first ping. This time, the ping is received 8 seconds after it is sent. How deep is the ocean floor in this location?

   A. 190 meters

   B. 380 meters

   C. 6,080 meters

   D. 12,160 meters

3. An oceanographer sends another ping every kilometer. He works in a grid pattern until he has depth readings from a 10 kilometer square area. How could he improve the bathymetric map that he produces?

   A. Make the pings louder.

   B. Make the pings softer.

   C. Make the pings farther apart.

   D. Make the pings closer together.

4. Oceanic trenches and mid-ocean ridges occur at

   A. tectonic plate centers.

   B. tectonic plate boundaries.

   C. guyots.

   D. rift valleys.

5. Which of the following can be seen above water?

   A. seamounts

   B. islands

   C. guyots

   D. both A and C

1. Ⓐ Ⓑ Ⓒ Ⓓ
2. Ⓐ Ⓑ Ⓒ Ⓓ
3. Ⓐ Ⓑ Ⓒ Ⓓ
4. Ⓐ Ⓑ Ⓒ Ⓓ
5. Ⓐ Ⓑ Ⓒ Ⓓ

Chapter 11
Ocean Movement I: Tides

GEORGIA 6TH GRADE CRCT IN SCIENCE STANDARDS COVERED IN THIS CHAPTER INCLUDE:

S6E3d	Explain the causes of waves, currents, and tides.

Bodies of water are in constant motion. For instance, rivers and streams run downhill — or more accurately, from areas of higher elevation to areas of lower elevation. Oceans, however, are very different than rivers; ocean water does not move in response to elevation. Because they cover such a large area, oceans respond to more global forces, namely, the motion of our planet. This kind of ocean movement is called tidal movement. **Tides** cause the bulk movement of water — that is, they cause water to alternately advance and recede.

TIDES

The word "tides" is a term used to define the rise and fall in sea level with respect to the land. It is produced by the gravitational attraction of both the Moon and the Sun. Tides also occur in large lakes, the atmosphere, and within the solid crust of the Earth.

Tides are created because the Earth and the Moon are attracted to each other, just like magnets are attracted to each other. The Moon tries to pull at anything on the Earth to bring it closer. But, the Earth is able to hold onto everything except the water. Since the water is always moving, the Earth cannot hold onto it, and the Moon is able to pull at it. Each day, there are two high tides and two

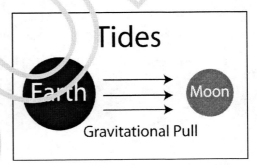

Figure 11.1 How Tides Form

low tides. The ocean is constantly moving from high tide to low tide, and then back to high tide. There are about 12 hours and 25 minutes between the two high tides.

When the Sun and Moon are aligned, there are exceptionally strong gravitational forces, causing very high and very low tides, which are called **spring tides**, though they have nothing to do with the season. Spring tides only occur during the full moon and the new moon. When the Sun and Moon are not aligned, the gravitational forces cancel each other out, and the tides are not as dramatically high and low. These are called **neap tides**.

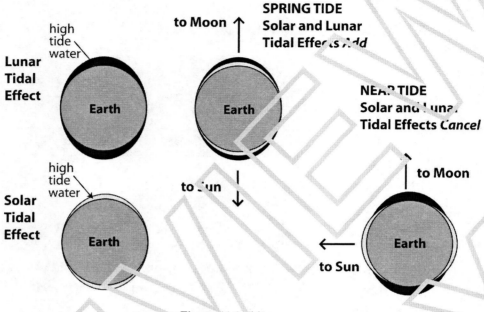

Figure 11.1 Tides

SCTF (SOME COOL TIDE FACTS)

- The gravitational force of the Moon is one ten-millionth that of Earth, but when you combine other forces such as the Earth's centrifugal force created by its spin, you get tides.

- The Sun's gravitational force on the Earth is only 46 percent that of the Moon. This makes the Moon the single most important factor for the creation of tides.

- Spring tides happen when the Sun and Moon are on the same side of the Earth (new moon) or when the Sun and Moon are on opposite sides of the Earth (full moon).

- When the Moon is at first quarter or last **quarter phase** (meaning that it is located at right angles to the Earth-Sun line), the Sun and Moon interfere with each other. These generally weaker tides are called neap tides.

- Spring tides and neap tide levels are about 20% higher or lower than average.

- Offshore, in the deep ocean, the difference in tides is usually less than 0.5 meters.

- The surf grows when it approaches a beach and the tide increases. In bays and estuaries, this effect is amplified. (In the Bay of Fundy, tides can be as high as 44.6 ft.)

- Since the Moon moves around the Earth, it is not always in the same place at the same time each day. So, each day, the times for high and low tides change by 50 minutes.

Chapter 11 Practice Questions

1. During spring tides, the gravitational pulls of the Sun and Moon may

    A. add to one another making tides exceptionally high and low.

    B. cancel each other out making tides neither high nor low.

    C. only be noticed in the deep ocean.

    D. cause exceptionally violent tides.

2. Tides are most affected by which of the following?

    A. the gravitational pull of the Sun

    B. the gravitational pull of the Moon

    C. the rotation of the Earth

    D. the occurrence of lunar eclipses

3. Neap tides occur when the Sun and Moon

    A. are lined up Sun, Moon, Earth.

    B. are at a 90° angle to one another.

    C. are lined up Sun, Earth, Moon.

    D. are aligned as in either A or B

4. How long does it take the Moon to complete one orbit around the Earth?

    A. 27 hours

    B. 24 hours

    C. 30 days

    D. 27 days

5. The Sun's gravitational force is about what percentage of the Moon's gravitational force?

    A. 54%

    B. 92%

    C. 46%

    D. 200%

1. Ⓐ Ⓑ Ⓒ Ⓓ
2. Ⓐ Ⓑ Ⓒ Ⓓ
3. Ⓐ Ⓑ Ⓒ Ⓓ
4. Ⓐ Ⓑ Ⓒ Ⓒ
5. Ⓐ Ⓒ Ⓒ Ⓓ

Mini - Review

Define these terms:

tide

_____

_____

spring tide

_____

_____

neap tide

_____

_____

quarter phase

_____

_____

Chapter 12
Ocean Movement II: Waves and Currents

GEORGIA 6TH GRADE CRCT IN SCIENCE STANDARDS COVERED IN THIS CHAPTER INCLUDE:

S6E3d	Explain the causes of waves, currents, and tides.
S6E4a	Demonstrate that land and water absorb and lose heat at different rates and explain the resulting effects on weather patterns.
S6E4b	Relate unequal heating of land and water surfaces to form large global wind systems and weather events such as tornados and thunderstorms.
S6E6a	Explain the role of the Sun as the major source of energy and its relationship to wind and water energy.

In the last section you discovered that tides are primarily a result of the gravitational attraction of the Earth and the Moon — that is, they are a *lunar* phenomenon. In this section we will look at a *solar* phenomenon – wind – and see how it causes a very different kind of ocean movement.

SOLAR RADIATION – HEAT FROM THE SUN

As you probably already know, the Earth receives its heat from the Sun. The Sun's energy is spread through the atmosphere in three ways – **radiation**, **convection**, and **conduction**.

RADIATION
Radiant energy from the Sun reaches Earth in a process called **radiation**. In this process, light waves from the Sun are absorbed by the Earth and returned to the atmosphere as heat. The Sun's rays do heat the air directly, but the majority of radiation's thermal heat impact is felt when it reaches solid ground or liquid water.

CONVECTION
Convection is the process through which heat is transferred by moving air or water. As air molecules absorb heat from the ground, the atoms contained within them move faster, and farther apart. As they spread out, the warm air becomes less dense, which means it is lighter, and it begins to rise (think of a hot-air balloon). As the warm air

rises, denser, heavier, and colder air moves in to replace it. This movement creates a **convection current**. Convection currents cause a constant exchange of air until the surface is evenly heated. Most of the heat in the Earth's atmosphere is transferred by convection currents.

CONDUCTION

The direct transfer of heat energy by contact is called **conduction**. When cool air above the Earth's surface comes into contact with the warm ground, the air is heated. That is why air temperatures closer to the ground are generally warmer than those higher up. Overall, however, conduction of heat from land and water to the atmosphere occurs over short distances. Like radiation, it plays a minor role in heating the atmosphere.

WIND AND OCEAN CURRENTS

Although land and water are poor long-range conductors of heat, they do move thermal energy efficiently enough to create **currents**. As radiation from the Sun passes through our atmosphere, it strikes the surface of the Earth. The radiant energy is absorbed, heating the ground. Air in contact with the ground is warmed by conduction. This air then expands and rises. Cooler, denser air from above moves in to replace this air, creating wind. The process of lifting warm air from Earth's surface to higher altitudes is an example of **convection**. The complete system of warm air rising and inflowing cold air replacing it is called a **convection current**.

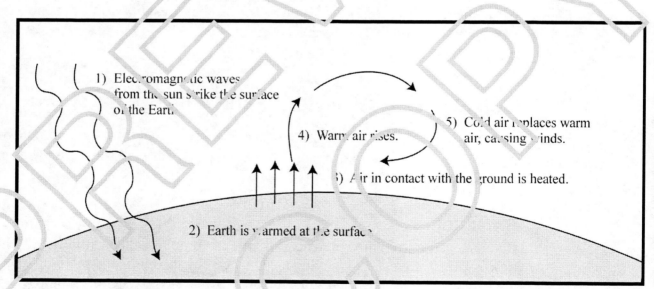

1) Electromagnetic waves from the sun strike the surface of the Earth.

4) Warm air rises.

5) Cold air replaces warm air, causing winds.

3) Air in contact with the ground is heated.

2) Earth is warmed at the surface.

Figure 12.1 Formation of Convection Currents

If we look at convection currents in terms of energy, convection would be the change of radiant energy into wind energy. Convection currents are enhanced by the different heating characteristics (**heat absorption rates**) of land and water. Land heats and cools much quicker than water, so changes in temperature are more dramatic over land surfaces than over bodies of water. The warm air found in the tropics creates consistent winds that move in a fairly constant direction.

Convection currents also have an effect on **surface ocean currents**. Surface ocean currents are created when the atmosphere and the ocean come in contact. The energy created by the convection cell in the air causes friction between the surface of the water and the moving air. This friction causes the water to move. Winds are the primary driving force of surface ocean currents. **Current** is the movement of the surface layer of water in response to the force of the winds above it. The diagram below shows other ocean currents on Earth. One current that you may be familiar with is the **Gulf Stream**. This powerful Atlantic Ocean current circulates warm water up the east coast of the U.S., continuing in a circular motion across the Atlantic Ocean. The Gulf Stream is primarily driven by winds.

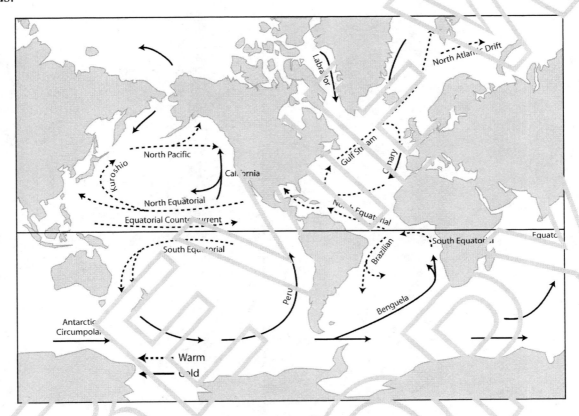

Figure 12.2 Ocean Currents

Winds are also partially responsible for creating ocean waves. Once again, if we look at this in terms of energy, radiant energy from the Sun is transferred into wind energy and that is transferred into mechanical wave energy. The Earth's rotation also affects winds and ocean currents. Visualize this: you have a top and you spin it very fast. Then you pick up a squirt gun and squirt water at the top as it spins. Where will the water go? As this the top it will move in the direction the top is moving. Now imagine the top is the Earth. In the Northern hemisphere, currents move to the right, or clockwise. In the Southern Hemisphere, the currents move to the left, or counterclockwise (from the perspective of a person standing in those places). This system of movement is called the **Coriolis Effect**.

Chapter 12 Practice Questions

1. The Sun's effect on the Earth is most pronounced at

   A. the Arctic Circle.

   B. the prime meridian.

   C. the equator.

   D. the Tropic of Capricorn.

2. Which type of thermal energy transfer best describes how the surface of the Earth is heated by the Sun?

   A. radiation

   B. solar wind

   C. conduction

   D. convection

3. Heat warms the atmosphere close to the Earth's surface. Warm air rises, and cooler air rushes in. This is a description of

   A. how winds are created.

   B. the pollution cycle.

   C. evaporation.

   D. element recycling.

4. Which mechanism of heat transfer has the most effect on heating the atmosphere of Earth?

   A. radiation

   B. solar winds

   C. conduction

   D. convection

5. Ocean currents move in different directions in different hemispheres. This is called

   A. the Coriolis Effect.

   B. the Doppler Effect.

   C. the Equatorial Force.

   D. the Centripetal Force.

1. (A) (B) (C) (D)
2. (A) (B) (C) (D)
3. (A) (B) (C) (D)
4. (A) (B) (C) (D)
5. (A) (B) (C) (D)

Chapter 13
Weather Patterns and Events

Georgia 6th Grade Crct in Science Standards covered in this chapter include:

S6E4c	Relate how moisture evaporating from the oceans affects the weather patterns and weather events such as hurricanes.

WEATHER VS. CLIMATE

You probably have heard these two terms used interchangeably, but there is a very important difference between them. When we talk about the **weather**, we are talking about daily or even hourly changes. **Climate**, on the other hand, is the averaging of those changes over long periods of time for a specific region. Six factors are considered when determining the weather and prevailing climate in an area. These factors are:

- air temperature
- humidity
- type and amount of cloudiness
- type and amount of precipitation
- air pressure
- speed and direction of wind.

Why are there different climates on Earth? It all has to do with the Earth's shape. As you know, the Earth is a sphere. When the Sun's rays hit the Earth, they strike different parts of the sphere at different angles. Think about shining a flashlight on a ball. Some areas would get direct light and some would get only partial light. It would be an uneven distribution. At the areas near the center the light would be the most direct. The same is true for the Earth. At the equator, the Sun is at a 90° angle in the sky, so that is where the climate is the warmest. At the Earth's poles exactly the opposite is true. The Sun barely makes it above the horizon — and right at the poles it doesn't even do that for almost half the year! That is why the polar climate is the coldest. In areas between the equator and the poles (geographers call that the **mid latitudes**) the temperature varies. The US fits into this category.

WEATHER PATTERNS

Air masses in the atmosphere are large bodies of air that have uniform temperature, moisture, and pressure. Think of these air masses as "blocks" of air. Air masses and their movements within the atmosphere cause most of the weather patterns in an area. In general there are six main air masses. Take a look at Figure 13.1 to see what they are and where they are located.

Air masses moving into an area from a tropical region tend to bring warm, moist air into that region. Tropical air usually brings humidity and rain. The movement of one air mass displaces another air mass and causes the formation of a front.

Figure 13.1 Air Masses

"Front"…kind of sounds like a battle line. In a sense it is. **Fronts** are boundaries that separate different air masses. Something you may not realize is that fronts extend not only in the horizontal direction, but in the vertical as well. There are four basic kinds of fronts:

- **Cold Front** - Leading edge of colder air that is replacing warmer air.
- **Warm Front** - Leading edge of warmer air that is replacing cooler air.
- **Stationary Front** - A front that is not moving.
- **Occluded Front** - When a cold front catches up to a warm front.

COLD FRONT

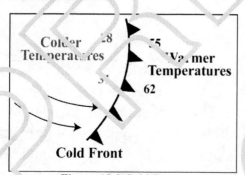

Figure 13.2 Cold Front

A **cold front** is the transition zone where a cold air mass is replacing a warmer air mass. Cold fronts generally move from northwest to southeast. The air behind a cold front is noticeably colder and drier than the air ahead of it. When a cold front passes through, temperatures can drop more than 15 degrees within the first hour. On a weather map, a cold front is represented by a solid line with triangles along the front pointing towards the warmer air and in the direction of movement.

WARM FRONT

A **warm front** is the transition zone where a warm air mass is replacing a cold air mass. Warm fronts generally move from southwest to northeast and the air behind a warm front is warmer and more moist than the air ahead of it. When a warm front passes through, the air becomes noticeably warmer and more humid than it was before. On a weather map, a warm front is represented by a solid line with semicircles pointing towards the colder air and in the direction of movement.

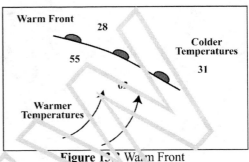

Figure 13.3 Warm Front

STATIONARY FRONT

When a warm or cold front stops moving, it becomes a **stationary front**. When this boundary resumes its forward motion on both sides, it once again becomes a warm front or cold front. On a weather map a stationary front is represented by alternating blue and red lines with blue triangles pointing towards the warmer air and red semicircles pointing towards the colder air.

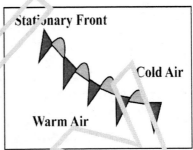

Figure 13.4 Stationary Front

OCCLUDED FRONT

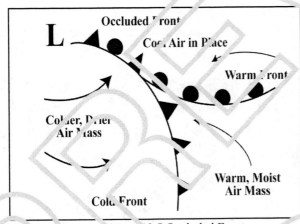

Figure 13.5 Occluded Front

A developing cyclone typically has a warm front arriving before it (the leading edge of a warm moist air mass) and a faster moving cold front (the leading edge of a colder drier air mass) wrapping around the storm. North of the warm front is a mass of cooler air that was in place before the storm even entered the region. As the storm intensifies, the cold front rotates around the storm and catches the warm front. This forms an **occluded front**, which is the boundary that separates the new cold air mass (to the west) from the older cool air mass already in place north of the warm front. On a weather map, an occluded front is represented by a solid line with alternating triangles and circles, pointing the direction the front is moving.

Air masses create weather based on their particular characteristics. Differences in pressure, temperature, and moisture create different kinds of weather patterns. The greater the differences between the two air masses, the more intense the weather. During the spring, different kinds of air masses are more likely to encounter one another. Stable, cold, dry air may meet unstable, warm, moist air. In the United States, these two types of air masses are most likely to meet in the central area of the country. Severe weather, like thunderstorms, often forms here. The region from Nebraska to Northern Texas is actually known as **tornado alley** because of the frequency of these types of storms.

Tornadoes are swift moving, low pressure columns of highly destructive power. While they focus on relatively narrow areas, another low pressure type of storm does not — hurricanes

HURRICANES

Hurricanes form in certain areas of marine environments. Because of the record-breaking hurricane season of 2005, and Hurricane Katrina, Americans are very well acquainted with hurricanes. Do you know what a hurricane really is?

Hurricanes must have all of the following characteristics:

1. They are **tropical**, meaning that they are generated in tropical areas of the ocean near the equator.

2. They are **cyclonic**, meaning that their winds swirl around a central **eye**.

3. They are **low-pressure systems**. The eye of a hurricane is always a low-pressure area. The lowest barometric pressures ever recorded have occurred inside hurricanes.

4. The winds swirling around the center of the storm must have a sustained speed of at least 74 mph (119 kph).

Figure 13.6 shows what a hurricane looks like from above the Earth

These massive circulating storms are called **hurricanes** in the Atlantic Ocean, **typhoons** in the Pacific Ocean and **cyclones** in the Indian Ocean. The location has an effect other than the name. In the Northern Hemisphere, hurricanes turn north before being blown east. In the Southern Hemisphere, hurricanes turn south before being blown east. This is due to the Coriolis Effect discussed in Chapter 12.

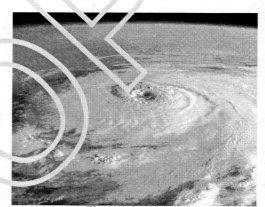

Figure 13.6 Hurricane

Chapter 13 Practice Questions

1. The greater the difference between two air masses, the _____ the weather.

    A. more severe

    B. less severe

    C. cooler

    D. calmer

2. Weather is

    A. very predictable.

    B. a term used to describe the atmosphere over a short period of time.

    C. a term used to describe the atmosphere over a long period of time.

    D. determined by temperature and humidity only.

3. Climate is

    A. very short term.

    B. the average of hourly temperatures over one day.

    C. the averaging of weather changes over long periods of time for a specific region.

    D. the average temperature over the entire Earth.

4. Two other names for hurricanes are

    A. monsoons and cyclones.

    B. typhoons and monsoons.

    C. cyclones and tornadoes.

    D. typhoons and cyclones.

5. Where is tornado alley?

    A. the region spanning Nebraska to Georgia

    B. the region spanning Nebraska to Texas

    C. the state of Texas

    D. The state of Nebrask

1. Ⓐ Ⓑ Ⓒ Ⓓ
2. Ⓐ Ⓑ Ⓒ Ⓓ
3. Ⓐ Ⓑ Ⓒ Ⓓ
4. Ⓐ Ⓑ Ⓒ Ⓓ
5. Ⓐ Ⓑ Ⓒ Ⓓ

Mini - Review

Describe the air masses and fronts shown in the weather map below, from the point of view of someone in Georgia.

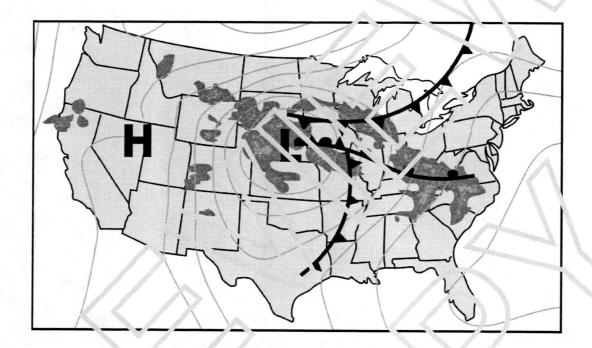

Domain Two Review

Choose the best answer for each Review question. Bubble in your answers in the space provided on the answer sheet below.

1. Ⓐ Ⓑ Ⓒ Ⓓ   11. Ⓐ Ⓑ Ⓒ Ⓓ

2. Ⓐ Ⓑ Ⓒ Ⓓ   12. Ⓐ Ⓑ Ⓒ Ⓓ

3. Ⓐ Ⓑ Ⓒ Ⓓ   13. Ⓐ Ⓑ Ⓒ Ⓓ

4. Ⓐ Ⓑ Ⓒ Ⓓ   14. Ⓐ Ⓑ Ⓒ Ⓓ

5. Ⓐ Ⓑ Ⓒ Ⓓ   15. Ⓐ Ⓑ Ⓒ Ⓓ

6. Ⓐ Ⓑ Ⓒ Ⓓ   16. Ⓐ Ⓑ Ⓒ Ⓓ

7. Ⓐ Ⓑ Ⓒ Ⓓ   17. Ⓐ Ⓑ Ⓒ Ⓓ

8. Ⓐ Ⓑ Ⓒ Ⓓ   18. Ⓐ Ⓑ Ⓒ Ⓓ

9. Ⓐ Ⓑ Ⓒ Ⓓ   19. Ⓐ Ⓑ Ⓒ Ⓓ

10. Ⓐ Ⓑ Ⓒ Ⓓ   20. Ⓐ Ⓑ Ⓒ Ⓓ

1. Transfer of heat is always from a higher temperature to a lower temperature. Cool air blowing over warm soil will result in

   A. warming of the soil.

   B. warming of the air.

   C. cooling of the soil.

   D. warming of the air and cooling of the soil.

2. If the maximum amplitude of ocean tides due to the Moon is 50 cm, and the maximum amplitude of ocean tides due to the Sun is 24 cm, what is the amplitude of the ocean tides that occur when the Sun and the Moon are in alignment with the Earth?

   A. 24 cm

   B. 26 cm

   C. 50 cm

   D. 74 cm

3. Which of the following weighs about 1 kilogram?

   A. a cup of water

   B. a liter of water

   C. a milliliter of water

   D. a kiloliter of water

4. The wind above the ocean water creates

   A. ocean waves and currents.

   B. waves only.

   C. currents only.

   D. neither waves or currents.

Use the following diagram to answer questions 5 and 6.

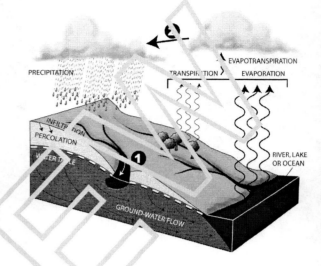

5. Two important processes in the water cycle are labeled with numbers 1 and 2. What are they?

   A. Condensation, depicted by arrow (1). Sublimation, depicted by arrow (2).

   B. Runoff, depicted by arrow (1). Sublimation, depicted by arrow (2).

   C. Runoff, depicted by arrow (1). Condensation, depicted by arrow (2).

   D. Condensation, depicted by arrow (1). Evaporation, depicted by arrow (2).

6. Note from the figure the similar roles of evaporation and transpiration. Evaporation describes the conversion of liquid water to water vapor. What is transpiration?

   A. The process by which plants respire.

   B. The process by which plants photosynthesize.

   C. The process by which plants release oxygen from their leaves.

   D. The process by which plants release water from their leaves and stems.

7. The speed of sound in water is
   A. 1520 m/s.
   B. 1520 km/s.
   C. 760 m/s.
   D. 760 km/s.

8. About what percentage of water on Earth is fresh water?
   A. 35%
   B. 71%
   C. 1%
   D. 3%

9. A ship pings a section of ocean floor. The ping is received 2 seconds after it is sent. About how deep is the ocean floor in this location?
   A. less than 1000 meters
   B. between 1,000 and 2,000 meters
   C. between 2,000 and 4,000 meters
   D. more than 4,000 meters

10. Brackish water contains
    A. more salt than ocean water.
    B. less salt than fresh water.
    C. more plankton than ocean water.
    D. more salt than fresh water.

11. One thing that oceanographers would not study is
    A. marine life in a hydrothermal vent.
    B. the eruption of an underwater volcano.
    C. the soil composition of an island.
    D. the formation of a new seamount.

12. Which of the following statements about currents and tides is correct?
    A. The Moon is primarily responsible for tidal patterns on Earth.
    B. The Sun is primarily responsible for tidal patterns on Earth.
    C. The Moon is primarily responsible for current patterns on Earth.
    D. A and C are both correct.

13. Salinity refers to
    A. the movement of ocean currents.
    B. the concentration of salt in water.
    C. the amount of heat released from hydrothermal vents.
    D. the study of the topography of the ocean floor.

14. The World Ocean is subdivided into 5 major oceans. Which of the following is not a recognized ocean?
    A. the Southern
    B. the Arctic
    C. the Antarctic
    D. the Indian

15. What defines the boundaries that subdivide the five oceans from the World Ocean?
    A. tidal movements
    B. subsurface topology
    C. ocean currents
    D. all of the above

16. What kind of front is shown in the figure below?

A. warm front

B. cold front

C. occluded front

D. secluded front

17. Where have the lowest barometric pressures ever recorded occurred?

A. in the center of a tornado

B. in the warm front preceding a hurricane

C. in the eye of a cyclone

D. along the line of a stationary front

18. The deepest parts of the ocean are

A. trenches.

B. rift valleys.

C. guyots.

D. hydrothermal vents.

19. Which ocean separates Antarctica from Australia?

A. the Arctic Ocean

B. the Southern Ocean

C. the Indian Ocean

D. the Pacific Ocean

20. How does a lake differ from a gulf?

A. A gulf is always fresh water, whereas a lake may contain fresh water.

B. A gulf is always salt water, whereas a lake may contain salt water.

C. A gulf is always salt water, whereas a lake is always fresh water.

D. A gulf is always fresh water, whereas a lake is never fresh water.

Domain Three
Geology

DOMAIN THREE COVERS:

Chapter 14 – Earth's Age

Chapter 15 – The Layers of the Earth

Chapter 16 – Plate Tectonics

Chapter 17 – Rocks and Rock Cycle

Chapter 18 – Weathering and Erosion

Chapter 19 – Soil Formation and Composition

Chapter 20 – The Effect of Human Activity

Chapter 21 – Resource Use

Chapter 14
Earth's Age

GEORGIA 6TH GRADE CRCT IN SCIENCE STANDARDS COVERED IN THIS CHAPTER INCLUDE:

S6E5g	Describe how fossils show evidence of the changing surface and climate of the Earth.

EARTH'S AGE

How old is the Earth?

Before we could even begin to answer this question, scientists had to come up with some pretty creative measurement techniques. All of these techniques rely, to some extent, on **estimation** — some educated guesses have to be made. Every estimate has a margin of error that comes along with it. The **margin of error** gives us a feel for how close the estimate is to the "real" value of the measurement.

Here is an example. Hospital records will indicate the time of your birth to the minute, as in "Judith Thompson was born on April 29, 1995 at 4:51 am." The time listed is actually a measurement. If the margin of error is included, the time might be stated "at 4:51 am, plus or minus (+/–) 50 seconds."

Well, when the time that we are trying to estimate (that is, the time when the Earth was formed) is a few billion years ago, the margin of error gets pretty large. In order to make the most accurate measurement, scientists check the results of one technique against the results of another.

There are many tools that scientist use to estimate the age of the Earth. Two of these are **superposition** (doesn't that sound sciency!) and the **fossil record**. Let's look at how scientists obtain information with these tools.

THE LAW OF SUPERPOSITION

This may sound complicated, but all it means is that when it comes to **rock strata** (layers of sedimentary rock), each layer is older than the layer above it. To put it another way, layers get older as you go downward, and more recent as you go upward. This kind of dating technique is called **relative dating** because it allows you to know the order in which layers formed, or, how old a layer is relative to other layers.

Take a look at Figure 14.1 and you'll notice that a layer of shale lies beneath a unit of limestone. Using what you just learned, you should understand that the shale is older than the limestone.

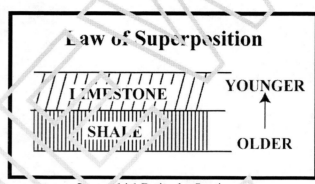

Figure 14.1 Dating by Stratigraphy

THE FOSSIL RECORD

Fossils can also be useful in deciphering geologic time. What is a fossil? It is the recognizable remains or body impressions of an organism that lived in the past. The **fossil record** refers to all fossils that have been found since the study of fossils began. Some fossils are recognized as unique to certain time periods. These are called **index fossils**. When an index fossil is found in a unit of sedimentary rock, the age of the rock is assumed to be the same as the age of the fossil.

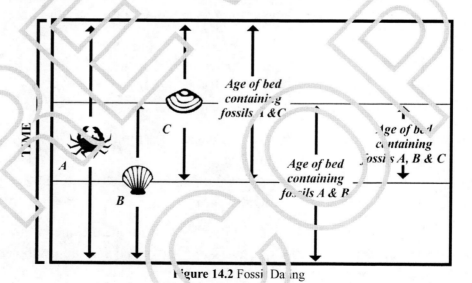

Figure 14.2 Fossil Dating

Where do fossils come from? Most come from organisms that have hard body parts. Things like **bone** or **shells** will fossilize more easily than flesh or tissue. That means that organisms like crabs or triceratops will more easily form fossils than, say, a jelly fish.

Even organisms that do have hard body parts may not get a chance to fossilize. The bones or shells may be destroyed by some geological event or scattered by animals. Occasionally, the conditions are right for fossil formation. Fossils are more likely to form when animals are buried very quickly. Catastrophic events, like **floods**, **mudslides** and **ash deposition** from volcanoes and earthquakes usually lead to the formation of fossils. The rarity of fossils makes each one valuable to scientific thought. In fact, estimates indicate that the fossil record only represents about 0.1% of all the organisms that have lived on the planet. It is important to note that no one knows exactly how many organisms have lived or do currently live on Earth.

So, back to our original question:

<h2 style="text-align:center">How old is the Earth?</h2>

 Now that you know more about how scientists have worked on the question, we'll finally give you the answer you are looking for. Using the methods in this section, scientists have determined that the Earth as is between 4.4 and 4.6 billion years old.

Chapter 14 Practice Questions

Use the following diagram to answer questions 1 – 3.

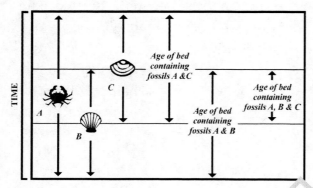

1. Which of the fossils indicated in the diagram is the youngest?

   A. fossil A

   B. fossil B

   C. fossil C

   D. This question cannot be answered without an accurate timeline.

2. If each division of the figure represents a 50 million year segment of time, which fossils might have been living on Earth the longest?

   A. fossil A

   B. fossil B

   C. fossil C

   D. Fossil B and C were equally long-lived.

3. The fossils in the figure are different varieties of ocean-dwelling mollusk or arthropod. These fossils were found on top of a mountain. What is the most likely conclusion?

   A. That crabs and mussels used to live on land.

   B. That crabs and mussels used to live at high altitudes.

   C. That the mountain was once submerged under the ocean.

   D. That the mountain was once the only home of crabs and mussels.

4. Which of the following organisms is least likely to fossilize?

   A. a chipmunk   C. a garden snake

   B. a beetle   D. an earthworm

5. The Earth is

   A. about 14 billion years old.

   B. about 4.5 billion years old.

   C. older than the oldest fossils.

   D. described by both answer B and C.

1. (A) (B) (C) (D)
2. (A) (B) (C) (D)
3. (A) (B) (C) (D)
4. (A) (B) (C) (D)
5. (A) (B) (C) (D)

Chapter 15
The Layers of the Earth

GEORGIA 6TH GRADE CRCT IN SCIENCE STANDARDS COVERED IN THIS CHAPTER INCLUDE:

S6E5a	Compare and contrast the Earth's crust, mantle, and core including temperature, density, and composition
S6E5b	Investigate the contribution of minerals to rock composition.

THE EARTH'S LAYERS

Now that you know how scientists attack the question of Earth's age, it's time to move on to more practical questions: Of what is Earth made? How does the Earth "work?"

Although the earth appears to be made up of solid rock, it's actually made up of three distinct layers: the **crust**, **mantle**, **and core**.

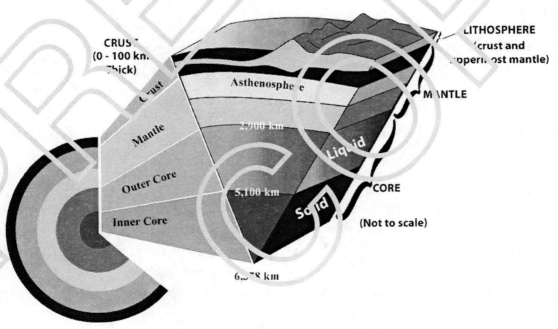

Figure 15.1 Layers of the Earth

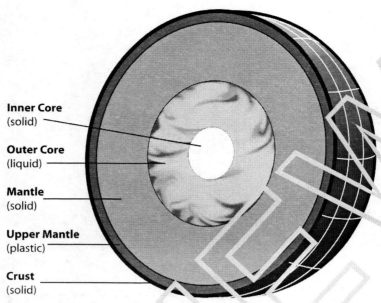

Inner Core
(solid)

Outer Core
(liquid)

Mantle
(solid)

Upper Mantle
(plastic)

Crust
(solid)

Figure 15.2 Cross Section of the Earth

CRUST

The **crust** is the thin, solid, outermost layer of the Earth, composed mainly of basalt and granite. **Oceanic crust** is generally thin, around 10 kilometers (km) thick. **Continental crust** is variable in thickness, and averages about 30 – 35km. All continents have some areas of thicker crust (40 – 50 km), usually concentrated under and around mountain ranges. Crust measurements of over 50 km are exceedingly rare in surveyed areas.

MANTLE

The layer below the crust is the **mantle**. The boundary that separates the two layers is called the **Mohorovicic discontinuity**, or **Moho** for short. The mantle is much thicker that the crust, extending from 30km to about 2,900 km. The mantle has more iron and magnesium than the crust, making it more dense. The uppermost part of the mantle is solid and, along with the crust, forms the **lithosphere**. The rocky lithosphere is brittle and can fracture. This is the zone where earthquakes occur. It's the lithosphere that breaks into the thick, moving slabs of rock that geologists call **tectonic plates**

As we move toward the center of the Earth to the lower mantle, the temperature rises and we reach part of the mantle that is partially **molten**. Molten means the rock is so hot it acts like plastic and can be stretched, folded, or even flow (although it's a pretty slow flow) without fracturing or breaking. This "mid-mantle" area is called the asthenosphere. The **asthenosphere** is the area of the mantle that is cooling by **convection**. Going deeper into the lower mantle, temperatures rise until we reach the liquid outer core.

CORE

At the center of the Earth lies the super-dense **core**. The core of the Earth is made up of two distinct layers: a liquid outer core and a solid inner core. Unlike the Earth's outer layer with rocky compositions, the core is made up of two metals, iron and nickel. It's hard to imagine, but the core is about 5 times as dense as the rock we walk on at the surface!

COMPOSITION OF THE EARTH

Table 15.1 summarizes the characteristics of Earth's layers. If you are confused by the entries under "composition," look at a Periodic Table: those are element abbreviations!

Table 15.1 Earth's Layers Described

Layer	Division	Approximate Range	Approximate Thickness	Composition	Temperature
Crust	Continental	0 – 10 km	30 km	Si, Al, Ca Fe, Mg, Na and K oxides	Dependent on location, subzero to over 100° C
	Oceanic	0 – 35 km			
Mantle	Lithosphere (crust + uppermost mantle)	0 – 75 km	2,870 km	Mostly Si, Fe and Mg oxides	100° C
	Asthenosphere (upper and mid mantle)	75 – 700 km			100° – 2,200° C
	Lower mantle	700 – 2,900 km			
Core	Outer	2,900 – 5,150 km	3,450 km	Fe and Ni	2,200° – 5000° C
	Inner	5,150 – 6,350 km			5000° C

Until you get to a Periodic Table, though, here is some help. The Earth's crust is composed of silicon (Si), aluminum (Al), calcium (Ca), iron (Fe), magnesium (Mg), sodium (Na) and potassium (K) oxides. An oxide is any element (like silicon) that forms a chemical compound with the element oxygen (O). For instance, silicon and oxygen form a **mineral** that you know as sand (SiO_2).

Chapter 15 Practice Test

1. The Moho forms a boundary between which two layers of the Earth?

   A. the lithosphere and the asthenosphere

   B. the crust and the mantle

   C. the upper mantle and the lower mantle

   D. the outer core and the lower mantle

2. Which layer of the Earth is the most dense?

   A. the crust

   B. the lower mantle

   C. the outer core

   D. the inner core

3. Which layer of the Earth is liquid?

   A. upper mantle

   B. lower mantle

   C. outer core

   D. inner core

4. What two kinds of crust are there?

   A. lithospheric and asthenospheric

   B. silicon based and iron based

   C. continental and oceanic

   D. outer and inner

5. Which layer of the Earth is the hottest?

   A. lithosphere

   B. asthenosphere

   C. outer core

   D. inner core

1. (A) (B) (C) D
2. (A) (B) (C) D
3. (A) (B) (C) D
4. (A) (B) (C) (D)
5. (A) (B) (C) (D)

Chapter 16
Plate Tectonics

S6E5e	Recognize that lithospheric plates constantly move and cause major geological events on the earth's surface

PLATE TECTONICS

The crust is broken into two types: **continental crust** and **oceanic crust**. As you probably have guessed, the continental crust contains the continents, and the oceanic crust is the Earth's crust at the bottom of the oceans. The lithosphere is divided into 14 large plates, which are interlocked with many smaller plates. The large plates are shown in Figure 16.1. Each plate moves as an individual unit. The tectonic plates, which are made of the relatively light, rigid rock of the lithosphere, actually 'float' on the denser, flowing athenosphere. The study of how these plates interact is called **plate tectonics**. The plate tectonic theory is a relatively new theory that combines two older theories: **continental drift** and **seafloor spreading**.

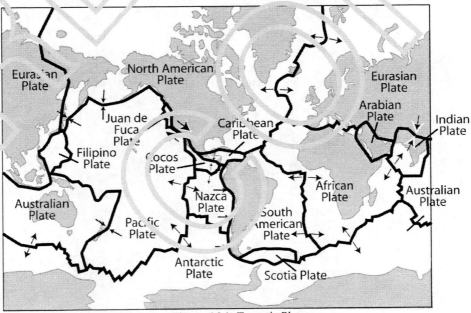

Figure 16.1: Tectonic Plates

Scientists believe that at one time in the past (about 200 million years ago), all of Earth's continents were joined in one gigantic "supercontinent" called **Pangaea**. Imagine being able to walk from Moscow to Dallas without having to get on a plane or boat! According to the theory of plate tectonics, the movement of the plates caused continents to drift apart in the process known as **continental drift**.

Figure 16.2 Pangaea

Convection currents that come from deep within the mantle may provide the energy that drives plate tectonics. These massive currents rotate in circular patterns, carrying heated rock upward. The molten rock soon reaches the crust. Where the crust is thin, as oceanic crust is, the molten rock may break through a crack. The hot magma (liquid rock) contacts ocean water. Then it hardens and becomes new rock. This process is called **seafloor spreading**. The underwater land formation that results is called a **mid-ocean ridge**. Mid-ocean ridges contain young rock, whereas other areas of the ocean floor contain older rock. The oldest rock is found on the continental crust.

When the convection currents bring magma up under the thicker continental crust, it doesn't usually break through; instead, it changes direction and moves underneath to the crust. This horizontal movement may drag the Earth's plates and carry the continents along with the underlying material. As the heated material cools, it sinks back into the mantle. New molten rock rises to continue the process.

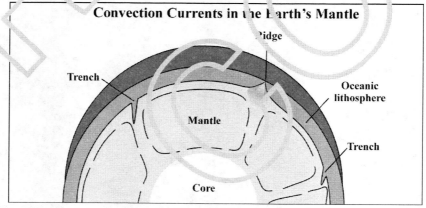

Figure 16.3

The **gravitational pull** of the Earth's heavy core may also contribute to the movement of material within the Earth. As you may remember from an earlier chapter, the gravitational force between two objects increases as the mass of the objects increases. Density is related to mass by the following equation:

$$D = \frac{m}{V}$$

The gravitational pull is greater on materials with a greater density. So, less dense materials have weaker gravitational forces exerted on them. As a result, materials of greater density such as iron and nickel tend to sink toward the center of the Earth.

PLATE BOUNDARIES

Let's take a closer look at what causes the tectonic plates to move. **Plate boundaries** are located where plates come together. There are three types of plate boundaries: **divergent**, **convergent**, and **transform**.

Divergent boundaries occur where two plates move apart from each other. As the plates move away from each other, magma erupts between them and creates new crust. As you now know, this type of boundary occurs mainly on the floor of the sea.

Convergent boundaries occur where two plates push together, causing one of the plates to sink into the mantle. A **subduction zone** forms where the plate sinks. The sinking plate melts and the other plate bends, creating a trench. Magma generated by the melting rock in the asthenosphere rises below the overriding plate, creating mountain ranges. Volcanic activity is common in subduction zones.

Transform boundaries occur where two plates slide past each other. Earthquakes are a common result of plates rubbing together at transform boundaries.

Divergent   **Convergent**   **Transform**

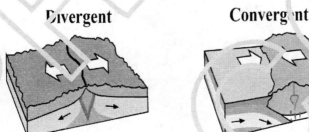
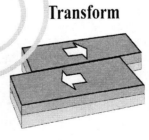

Figure 16.4 Plate Boundary Types

FOLDING

Folds are bends in rocks. Rocks create folds when forces in the Earth press land inward. A great way to visualize this is to take a towel that is folded several times, lay it out flat, and then smush it inward on both ends. You should see folds (hills and valleys) in the towel. The geological process takes much longer and happens much slower than the one with your towel.

Folding occurs along convergent plate boundaries and is one way that mountains are created.

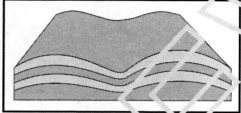

Figure 16.5 Folding

FAULTING

A **fault** is a fracture, or break, in the Earth's crust. On each side of the fracture, the rocks move relative to each other. **Faulting** occurs when bodies of rock slide past one another, with either a vertical (up and down) motion or a horizontal (side to side) motion. Faulting can occur abruptly or over long periods of time. Faulting at a plate boundary often results in an **earthquake**, the sudden movement of the Earth's crust. Think of it this way: as you go downward into the fault, you find two "sticky" surfaces of rock squeezed together, but having to slide past one another. The sticky, hot rock at lower depths of the fault keeps the faults from moving past one another until finally the pressure to move (remember what you learned about tectonic plates) is too great to be ignored. When the movement does happen, it is forceful and causes movement all along and around the fault…this is an earthquake.

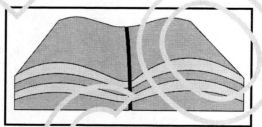

Figure 16.6 Faulting

Chapter 16 Practice Questions

1. When two plates converge, one plate is usually forced to slide under the other. Oceanic plates are more dense than continental plates. If an oceanic plate collides with a continental plate, what will be the likely result?

   A. The continental plate will slide under the oceanic plate, generating an oceanic trench.

   B. The oceanic plate will slide under the continental plate, generating an oceanic trench.

   C. The continental plate will slide under the oceanic plate, generating an earthquake.

   D. The oceanic plate will slide under the continental plate, generating an earthquake.

2. If two plates meet at a convergent boundary and *do not* form a subduction zone, they may

   A. fold.

   B. fault.

   C. weather.

   D. erupt.

3. The process of seafloor spreading occurs at what kind of plate boundary?

   A. divergent

   B. convergent

   C. transform

   D. at both convergent and transform boundaries

4. Where does magma come from?

   A. the inner core

   B. the outer core

   C. the mantle

   D. the lithosphere

5. The ancient supercontinent, Pangea, once contained

   A. all of the Earth's tectonic plates.

   B. all of the Earth's crust.

   C. all of the Earth's continental crust.

   D. all of the Earth's oceanic crust.

1. A B C D
2. A B C D
3. A B C D
4. A B C D
5. A B C D

Mini - Review

Describe the process occuring in the following diagram.

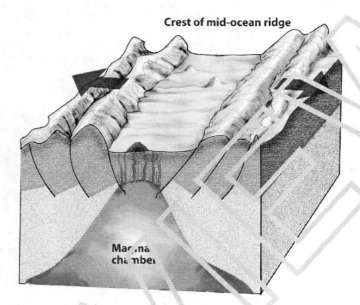

Crest of mid-ocean ridge

Magma chamber

Chapter 17
Rocks and the Rock Cycle

GEORGIA 6TH GRADE CRCT IN SCIENCE STANDARDS COVERED IN THIS CHAPTER INCLUDE:

S6E5c	Classify rocks by their process of formation.
S6E5d	Describe processes that change rocks and the surface of the Earth.
S6E5f	Explain the effects of physical processes (plate tectonics, erosion, deposition, volcanic eruption, gravity) on geological features including oceans (composition, currents, and tides).

ROCKS AND THE ROCK CYCLE

There are three types of rocks: **igneous**, **sedimentary**, and **metamorphic**. Igneous rocks are formed from magma beneath the Earth's surface. Sedimentary rocks are formed from deposited and compressed sediments. Metamorphic rocks are rocks that have been changed by heat and pressure.

IGNEOUS ROCKS

Igneous rocks result from the cooling of melted rock. They are of two types: intrusive or extrusive, depending on where they solidified. Igneous rocks that cool beneath Earth's surface generally contain large crystals and are called **intrusive** igneous rocks. **Extrusive** igneous rocks are formed when volcanoes spew magma (called **lava** when it reaches the surface), which then cools above the Earth's surface. Extrusive igneous rocks often occur as lava flows. Extrusive igneous rocks contain small crystals. They are sometimes composed of ash or glass because they cool very rapidly, unlike intrusive rocks.

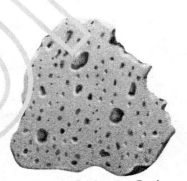

Figure 17.1 Igneous Rock

Figure 17.2 Sedimentary Rocks

SEDIMENTARY ROCKS

Sedimentary rocks are deposited in layers. They are found on land and in the water. On land, weathering of rocks create rock fragments. These are often transported from their weathering point and are then deposited, compacted and cemented together in layers at another location. These types of sedimentary rocks include **sandstone, mudstone,** and **conglomerates**.

The second type of sedimentary rock comes from ocean water. Changes in temperature cause minerals to deposit on the ocean floor as **sediments**, including **limestone, halite** (rock salt), and **gypsum**.

METAMORPHIC ROCKS

Metamorphic rocks are formed when the actual structure of a rock is changed. Often heat and pressure cause the change, but chemicals are agents of change as well. For example, when pressure is applied to sandstone, the sandstone compresses and forms a metamorphic rock called **quartzite**. Limestone, under heat and pressure, forms **marble**. Some minerals transform into completely different minerals through chemical changes.

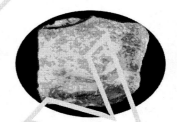

Figure 17.3 Metamorphic Rock

Metamorphic rock is typically unlayered. Water is an important component in chemical rock change because the water transports the chemicals that make the change take place.

THE ROCK CYCLE

Scientists use **rock cycle** as a model to describe rocks changes on the Earth. These changes show how each type of rock is formed. Some of the processes such as weathering, erosion and deposition occur at or near the Earth's surface. Other processes such as melting and increased heat and pressure occur deep below the surface. The rock cycle can begin with igneous rocks, created when magma cools and solidifies. Igneous rocks on the Earth's surface can undergo weathering and erosion, which creates **sediment**. Most sediment deposits are in oceans, but some ends up in river flood plains, desert basins, swamps and dunes. Sedimentary rocks develop from sediment (weathered and eroded rock) that becomes compacted and cemented together. Sedimentary and igneous rocks within the Earth can also be subject to heat and pressure (and from what you read earlier you should know that create metamorphic rock!). It doesn't always work this way, though; since it is a cycle, we could choose to begin anywhere! Let's start again with sedimentary and metamorphic rocks. Sometimes sedimentary and metamorphic rocks are exposed to weathering and erosion and create sediment.

The cycle also shows that it is possible for metamorphic, sedimentary and igneous rocks within the Earth to melt, forming magma. When magma is sent to the Earth's surface through volcanic action, the cycle (on the next page) begins again.

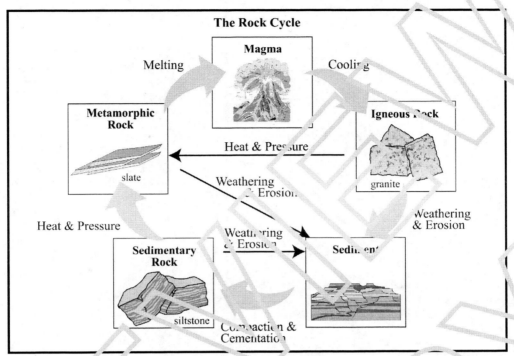

The Rock Cycle

Magma

Melting   Cooling

Metamorphic Rock

Igneous Rock

Heat & Pressure

slate   granite

Heat & Pressure   Weathering & Erosion   Weathering & Erosion

Sedimentary Rock   Weathering & Erosion   Sediment

siltstone   Compaction & Cementation

Figure 17.4 The Rock Cycle

VOLCANIC ACTIVITY

A **volcano** is a mountain formed from **lava** and rocks made from materials that have emerged from inside the earth. **Magma** is a combination of liquid rock material and dissolved gases deep within the Earth. The dissolved gases in magma are mostly water vapor, carbon dioxide, nitrogen and sulfur.

Magma is generated when solid rock from the crust is forced down into the Earth's asthenosphere at a **plate boundary**. Volcanoes typically occur at convergent plate boundaries.

Magma reaches the Earth's surface through an opening called a **vent** that begins deep inside the Earth. When magma reaches the Earth's surface, it is called **lava**. The lava flows out of the vent and as it hardens, it builds up and forms a mountainous structure. When the mountain is formed, the

Figure 17.5 Volcanic Vent

vent still has a way to release magma; it releases magma through a crater. The **crater** is the hole in the top of the volcano. A cross-section of a volcano is pictured in Figure 17.5.

Chapter 17 Practice Questions

1. Volcanoes are usually formed by the
   A. collision of transform plates.
   B. collision of convergent plates.
   C. rubbing together of transform plates.
   D. rubbing together of divergent plates.

2. The hole in the top of a volcano is called a
   A. vent.
   B. crater.
   C. magma boundary.
   D. lava valve.

3. Limestone and sandstone are examples of what kind of rock?
   A. igneous
   B. sedimentary
   C. metamorphic
   D. marble

4. Metamorphic rock is rock whose structure has changed. What factors change the rock?
   A. heat and pressure
   B. chemicals
   C. heat and pressure, or chemicals
   D. heat, pressure and chemicals

5. Cooling lava forms
   A. magma.
   B. intrusive igneous rock.
   C. extrusive igneous rock.
   D. metamorphic rock.

1. (A) (B) (C) (D)
2. (A) (B) (C) (D)
3. (A) (B) (C) (D)
4. (A) (B) (C) (D)
5. (A) (B) (C) (D)

Chapter 18
Weathering and Erosion

GEORGIA 6TH GRADE CRCT IN SCIENCE STANDARDS COVERED IN THIS CHAPTER INCLUDE:

S6E5d	Describe processes that change rocks and the surface of the earth.
S6E5i	Explain the effects of human activity on the erosion of the earth's surface.

WEATHERING

Not even rocks last forever on the Earth's surface. When a rock is broken down into smaller pieces it is called **weathering**. A rock **weathers** in response to changes in the environment. A rock buried in the Earth can remain the same for millions of years, but when exposed to wind and water at the Earth's surface, it will weather. Weathering can occur by three different methods: **mechanical weathering**, **chemical weathering** and **biological weathering**.

Mechanical weathering is a process where rocks are physically broken into smaller pieces by wind, water, ice or heat. The common product of mechanical weathering is silt, a form of very finely-ground rock.

Examples of this type of weathering are everywhere. For example, the Grand Canyon is a channel cut through rock by the powerfully surging waters of the Colorado River, over a period of many millions of years.

Figure 18.1 Channel in the Grand Canyon

Freezing and thawing cycles also weather rock mechanically. If you ever travel up the Eastern Seaboard to a northern state like New Jersey or New York, you find that the roads become bumpier and road maintenance more common. This is because the winters are colder up north. Why should that matter? Water gets into the cracks and crevices of concrete and asphalt (which are just processed rock). When the water freezes, it expands. The ice crystals push against the solid rock, weakening its structure. When it warms up again, the ice crystals melt and the pressure is released — but the rock structure is weakened even more. Each time the rock freezes and thaws, it cracks a little more, until it is rubble.

Chemical weathering is a process where minerals within the rocks are broken down by removing or altering elements that make up the minerals. The most common form of chemical weathering is the result of atmospheric carbon dioxide (CO_2). When the carbon dioxide combines with rain, they form a weak acid which reacts strongly with limestone formations, quickly dissolving them. **Clays** are a result of chemical weathering.

Biological weathering is weathering caused by living organisms and can occur by either mechanical or chemical means. For example, burrowing animals or plant roots can break up soil and rocks mechanically. Lichens chemically weather the rocks they live on by secreting enzymes that remove nutrients from the rock and reduce it to soil.

EROSION

Erosion is the transport of soil or rock by water, ice or wind. Erosion is one of the most often misused terms in science. Erosion is the **movement** of weathered rock, and NOT the actual weathering itself. Streams and rivers not only weather rocks, but they also transport the fragments downstream (erosion) by carrying them in the water or rolling them along the bottom. A river can alter its course, cutting a new channel. This type of erosion often occurs in the flood plains that have meandering river channels. Instead of continuing along its curvy route, a river can erode a channel through the sediments in the flood plain and create a straighter course. **Water erosion** also occurs along ocean shorelines. At the shore of the ocean, waves weather and transport rocks along the beaches. The December 26, 2004 **tsunami** (huge sea wave) in Southeast Asia caused tremendous loss of life and property. It also eroded beaches and land masses, moving sand and soil along the coasts of many countries.

Wind erosion is apparent all over the Earth but is most apparent in desert climates, where water is scarce. The wind picks up small pieces of rock fragments and carries them along until they reach an obstacle, such as a hill. The fragments, pushed by the wind, act as a sandblaster, eroding the hill slowly over time. The wind also causes erosion by scooping up large areas of loose soil and transporting it to another location.

One example of wind erosion in our own nation's history is the **Dust Bowl**. As settlers moved into the central United States, they removed the vast plains of grass to clear the area for farming. Poor farming techniques, combined with a drought, left the soil dry and loose. Wind erosion moved the dusty soil and destroyed much of the Great Plains.

Another form of erosion is **gravitational erosion**. This is where rock faces and outcropping are gradually pressed down the slope by their own weight.

Figure 18 2 The Dust Bowl

Chapter 18 Practice Questions

1. Wind causes weathering and erosion primarily because it

   A. transports chemicals.

   B. transports particles.

   C. transports microbes.

   D. causes rapid cooling.

2. Acid rain slowly dissolves statues and buildings. What is this action a good example of?

   A. mechanical weathering

   B. chemical weathering

   C. biological weathering

   D. erosion

3. What action of water causes rocks to crack?

   A. freezing

   B. thawing

   C. evaporation

   D. A and B

4. Water weathered the Grand Canyon

   A. mechanically.

   B. chemically.

   C. biologically.

   D. automatically.

5. A tree root breaks the asphalt on your driveway. This is a good example of

   A. mechanical weathering.

   B. chemical weathering.

   C. biological weathering.

   D. mechanical and biological weathering.

1. Ⓐ Ⓑ Ⓒ Ⓓ
2. Ⓐ Ⓑ Ⓒ Ⓓ
3. Ⓐ Ⓑ Ⓒ Ⓓ
4. Ⓐ Ⓑ Ⓒ Ⓓ
5. Ⓐ Ⓑ Ⓒ Ⓓ

Chapter 19
Soil Formation and Composition

S6E5h	Describe soil as consisting of weathered rocks and decomposed organic material.

In the previous chapter we discussed weathering -- the wearing away of rock by wind, rain, chemicals, plants and animals. The product of this process is **soil formation**. Here is how it works.

Tiny pieces are broken away from a large piece of rock and fall to the ground. Once there, the weathering continues. The tiny pieces are washed away by rainwater (eroded), and whittled and shaped by their collision with other objects. Over time, the tiny pieces become even tinier and form cracks and scratches in their surface. Bacteria and fungi make homes in these crevices, and produce chemicals that further weather the rock structure. This chemical action also releases minerals from the rock that fuel the growth of other organisms, including plants.

The plants grow, take up nutrients and minerals and eventually die. The plant is broken down by bacteria. Its remains are mostly **organic** (carbon-based). But they also contain those nutrients and minerals that the plant took up from the ground, which are **inorganic** (not carbon-based). Both organic and inorganic materials are deposited in the soil. The soil is enriched by both the **organic matter**, which results from the decay of living things like plants, and the **inorganic matter**, which results from the decay of non-living things like rocks.

These ongoing processes continue to develop the soil until, at some point, the soil can be called **mature.** Maturity is reached more quickly in hot, wet climates than in cold, dry climates. Mature soil has four layers, called **horizons**.

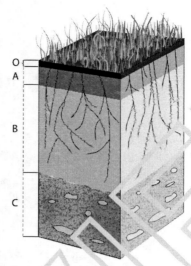

Figure 19.1 Horizons of Mature Soil

At the very top, above the soil line, is the **O horizon**. What do you think that "O" stands for? Organic! The O horizon is the organic layer, where plants live.

Just below that is the **A horizon**. This contains organic matter, including decaying plants, plant roots, etc. The A horizon is very rich in nutrients, and so it is also the home of many insects, worms and burrowing animals. This layer is called **topsoil**.

Next comes the **B horizon**, which contains clays and mineral deposits that have not yet been weathered. The structure of the subsoil will be gradually broken up by seeping water and intruding plant roots. The nutrients in this layer will be gradually incorporated into the A horizon as plant roots absorb them. This layer is called the **subsoil**.

Below that is the **C horizon**, containing weathered bedrock. This horizon is mostly isolated from the soil formation process. It is called the **substratum**.

Chapter 19 Practice Questions

1. Organic matter is

    A. carbon-based.

    B. oxygen-based.

    C. nitrogen-based.

    D. iron-based.

2. Which of the following contains the least organic matter?

    A. sticks

    B. leaves

    C. rocks

    D. acorns

Use the following diagram to answer questions 3 & 4.

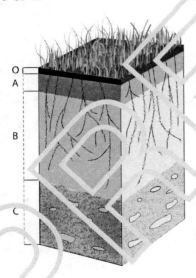

3. Which of the following contains the most organic matter?

    A. horizon A

    B. horizon B

    C. horizon C

    D. horizon O

4. Which horizon is called the subsoil?

    A. horizon A

    B. horizon B

    C. horizon C

    D. horizon O

5. Which of the following releases the nutrients in rocks, so that the minerals that they contain may be used by plants?

    A. the presence of bacteria and fungi

    B. the erosion of the rock

    C. the weathering of the rock

    D. the decay of organic matter

1. (A) (B) (C) (D)
2. (A) (B) (C) (D)
3. (A) (B) (C) (D)
4. (A) (B) (C) (D)
5. (A) (B) (C) (D)

Mini - Review

Use the diagram to illustrate the location of the soil horizons. Label them in the drawing, showing where you think they should go. Describe their composition — What's in each horizon?

Chapter 20
The Effects of Human Activity

© Copyright American Book Company. DO NOT DUPLICATE. 1-888-264-5877.

GEORGIA 6TH GRADE CRCT IN SCIENCE STANDARDS COVERED IN THIS CHAPTER INCLUDE:

S6E5i	Explain the effects of human activity on the erosion of the earth's surface.

Weathering and erosion produce soil, through a series of naturally-occurring processes. However, humans affect both weathering and erosion by their activities on the planet. Let's look at some of our activities, and their effects.

LOGGING

Humans use trees for a variety of reasons, including building and paper-making. **Logging** is the cutting of trees. Logging is usually done in dense forests that contain many trees. Sometimes people grow trees to cut them down, and sometimes the trees are part of a natural forest. Regardless, the most profitable and easiest method of logging is to **clear-cut** the given area — that is, to cut down all of the trees standing there. If the type of soil and its location are prone to erosion already, the environmental impact of clear-cutting can be huge. Without tree roots to hold down the soil, rain washes away the soil and the land becomes much more barren.

BUILDING

Building is going on everywhere around us — construction of roads, houses, skyscrapers and various other structures. Each of these projects alter the land itself in a particular way. Two components of this change are:

- Trees and plants are removed during construction.
- Soil is moved to accommodate construction.

The result is an increase in soil erosion during construction. Almost all urban areas require that sandbags and nylon fencing surround the construction site. This reduces soil loss, and lessens the amount of soil washed into storm drains. Once builders complete construction, they plant landscaping, which reduces soil erosion back to normal levels.

Unfortunately, building does change natural water pathways. Sidewalks and parking lots prevent water from percolating into the ground. Buildings placed on artificial hills increase water runoff. Buildings placed in artificial valleys require extensive drain construction to avoid pooling water and flooding. Fertilizers used in landscaping alter the absorption pattern of water. All of these are examples of how people divert water from its natural path, but the effects are not always easy to predict.

One remediation technique often employed by builders is the **siltation pond**. These structures are located in areas where there is high water runoff) for instance, paved urban developments like business parks and parking lots) or where there is a pollutant source (for instance, around landfill sites). Siltation ponds serve as a holding tank for water, before it dumps into the water system. Storm runoff drains directly into them; silt sinks to the bottom and the water forms a bond above it. Eventually, algae and other plants begin to grow in the pond.

Siltation ponds reduce the problems associated with building in three ways. First, they prevent silt from reaching the water system directly. Second, the aquatic life they contain cleans the water of many pollutants, naturally. Third, they lessen the threat of flooding during heavy rains.

MINING

Mining is the removal of material from the ground. When the target materials are close to the surface, they may be removed by a process called surface mining. **Surface mining** involves the use of great earth-moving machines to essentially peel back the surface of the Earth. The target material is removed, and the huge areas of open bedrock are exposed. **Strip-mining** and **open-pit** mining are examples of surface mining. Because surface mining techniques destroy the landscape, they are quite damaging to the local environment and greatly increase soil erosion.

Subsurface mining involves burrowing underneath the surface of the Earth to extract underground materials. This type of mining also alters the above-ground landscape because miners use explosives to create the tunnel and drive vehicles to remove the blasted rock. Erosion is increased in the vicinity of a mine. Also, the dust produced by drilling and blasting is an airborne pollutant.

Because our manufacturing requires the use of so many different kinds of minerals and raw resources, mining is a necessary part of American industry. Like logging and building, it is one which has a great many environmental consequences.

FARMING

Farming is a way of life for many people, and certainly all people benefit from the produce of farmers. But large tracts of farmland require a large commitment to substainable practices. Reducing water runoff and soil erosion are important in maintaining soil quality and, in turn, keeping crop yields high.

Many farmlands are surrounded by stands of tall trees. These serve to prevent winds from carrying off too much topsoil and are called **windbreaks**. In hilly areas, the soil is terraced into step-like formations. Crops are grown on the flat part of the step. **Soil terracing** lessens water runoff and preserves topsoil.

Irrigation of farmlands is also done carefully. Rather than use the sprinklers that are common in residential gardens, farmers employ log segments of soaker hoses. Reducing the spray of water into a stream of water keeps water loss by evaporation to a minimum.

Mini - Review

One effect of human activity is the introduction of pollutants into the environment. Discuss the effects of altering the carbon, water and nitrogen cycles and the biosphere.

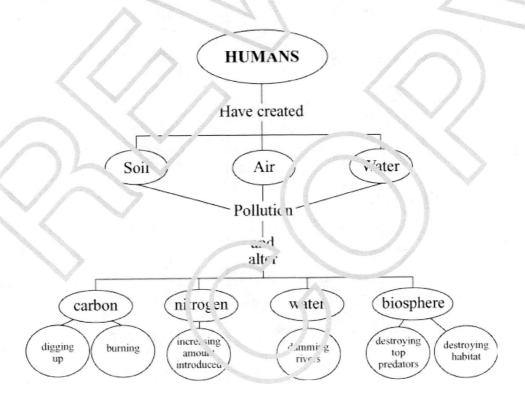

Chapter 20 Practice Questions

1. Strip-mining is environmentally damaging because

   A. it increases soil erosion.

   B. it decreases soil erosion.

   C. it weathers the subsoil.

   D. it pollutes the water.

2. Which of the following is mostly responsible for preventing erosion?

   A. weathering of rocks

   B. farming

   C. the presence of plants

   D. the removal of trees

3. Clear-cutting is a common practice in what industry?

   A. farming

   B. logging

   C. mining

   D. building

4. Sandbags and nylon fencing are placed around construction areas to

   A. increase soil erosion.

   B. decrease soil erosion.

   C. improve the appearance of the construction site.

   D. increase soil formation.

5. How do parking lots affect water pathways?

   A. They decrease the nutrients lost from the soil.

   B. They increase water absorption into the ground.

   C. They keep water from being absorbed into the ground.

   D. They stop erosion.

1. (A) (B) (C) (D)
2. (A) (B) (C) (D)
3. (A) (B) (C) (D)
4. (A) (B) (C) (D)
5. (A) (B) (C) (D)

Chapter 21
Resource Use

GEORGIA 6TH GRADE CRCT IN SCIENCE STANDARDS COVERED IN THIS CHAPTER INCLUDE:

| S6E5j | Describe methods for conserving natural resources such as water, soil, and air. |
| S6E6b | Identify renewable and nonrenewable resources. |

RESOURCE USE

Matter cannot be created or destroyed — it is a law of nature. There are a finite amount of natural resources available on the planet. Humans use **natural resources** (raw materials) to live. A natural resource can be considered renewable or non-renewable. **Non-renewable resources** like coal, oil and natural gas are replaced only after long periods of time and under certain conditions. **Renewable resources** can be replaced within the human lifetime.

Figure 21.1 A Clear-Cut Forest

Renewable resources include timber, water and solar energy. However, even renewable resources can be depleted. Too much logging can lead to timber shortages, and excessive water use can deplete the supply of fresh water. Strategies that help prevent depletion include reducing the amount of raw materials used, reusing products and recycling.

Natural resources are not evenly dispersed throughout the world. Nonrenewable resources form or accumulate over a long period of time, so that our present supply is considered a fixed amount. Nonrenewable resources were deposited in different locations on the planet as the Earth's crust evolved. For example, mineral deposits like aluminum and tin were moved as a result of plate tectonics. Processes like erosion concentrate the minerals in different areas of the Earth. When minerals are concentrated in a location, they can be mined.

Renewable resources, like bodies of water and forests, can be replenished over a short period of time. Renewable resources are also unevenly distributed.

Highly developed nations can buy resources that aren't available in their own country. For example, the United States buys oil from countries in the Middle East. Most people in the United States live in urban areas and buy food grown in other parts of the country or in other nations. This economic prosperity is not an option for many developing nations.

Humans use both renewable and nonrenewable resources inefficiently, thus depleting much of the supply. As the human population grows larger, the need to plan for the future and to protect resources becomes apparent. However, people have different ideas and opinions about how resources should be used. In developing nations, resources required for survival are generally small per person. In wealthier nations, individuals think that they need more than they actually need. Developed nations, like the United States, have "throwaway" lifestyles, and thus, overuse resources.

Americans have begun to realize that our lifestyles are wasteful. The United States has implemented several practices to help conserve and recycle. For example, Congress has passed soil conservation and timber replacement measures. Local laws often require reduced water consumption by installing showers and toilets that use less water and limiting water use for landscape activities. Research into using alternative energy sources will also help reduce the amount of fossil fuels used and may help find renewable energy sources. These are called **sustainable practices** — they are practices designed to use natural resources in a way that is not wasteful.

Chapter 21 Practice Questions

1. Earth's natural resources are

    A. evenly distributed.

    B. all in the poles.

    C. concentrated in different areas.

    D. all along the equator.

2. How can people reduce the amount of resources they use?

    A. Write to their congressional representative to ask for more landfills.

    B. Make sure that products use extra packaging materials so it is easier for people to use.

    C. Use water, electricity, and gas efficiently and recycle metal, paper, and glass.

    D. Think only about what you need right now and not about the big picture.

3. The benefits of international discussions about the environment are that

    A. the blame can be placed on the greatest polluter, and that country pays for cleanup.

    B. nations can create agreements to control pollution and protect the environment.

    C. wars can be started on those countries that don't follow environmental laws.

    D. the country with the most money can pay for pollution cleanup.

4. Which of the following activities is not a sustainable practice?

    A. turning off the water when you are not using it

    B. recycling aluminum cans

    C. drilling for oil

    D. saving rainwater

5. Which of the following is a renewable resource?

    A. coal

    B. natural gas

    C. timber

    D. mineral deposits

1. Ⓐ	Ⓑ	Ⓒ	Ⓓ
2. Ⓐ	Ⓑ	Ⓒ	Ⓓ
3. Ⓐ	Ⓑ	Ⓒ	Ⓓ
4. Ⓐ	Ⓑ	Ⓒ	Ⓓ
5. Ⓐ	Ⓑ	Ⓒ	Ⓓ

Mini - Review

What do the following two images have in common?

Solar Panels   Texas Wind Farm

Domain Three Review

Choose the best answer for each Review question. Bubble in your answers in the space provided on the answer sheet below.

1. Ⓐ Ⓑ Ⓒ Ⓓ
2. Ⓐ Ⓑ Ⓒ Ⓓ
3. Ⓐ Ⓑ Ⓒ Ⓓ
4. Ⓐ Ⓑ Ⓒ Ⓓ
5. Ⓐ Ⓑ Ⓒ Ⓓ
6. Ⓐ Ⓑ Ⓒ Ⓓ
7. Ⓐ Ⓑ Ⓒ Ⓓ
8. Ⓐ Ⓑ Ⓒ Ⓓ
9. Ⓐ Ⓑ Ⓒ Ⓓ
10. Ⓐ Ⓑ Ⓒ Ⓓ

11. Ⓐ Ⓑ Ⓒ Ⓓ
12. Ⓐ Ⓑ Ⓒ Ⓓ
13. Ⓐ Ⓑ Ⓒ Ⓓ
14. Ⓐ Ⓑ Ⓒ Ⓓ
15. Ⓐ Ⓑ Ⓒ Ⓓ
16. Ⓐ Ⓑ Ⓒ Ⓓ
17. Ⓐ Ⓑ Ⓒ Ⓓ
18. Ⓐ Ⓑ Ⓒ Ⓓ
19. Ⓐ Ⓑ Ⓒ Ⓓ
20. Ⓐ Ⓑ Ⓒ Ⓓ

1. The diagram indicates the approximate stratiography of the Paleozoic era. Northwest Georgia contains large deposits of Cambro-Ordovician dolostone and Ordovician limestone. Under the Cumberland Plateau in the far Northwest corner of the state, Carboniferous sandstone and shale can be found. Ochre has been mined from Cambrian dolostone in Cartersville. Which of these rock deposits lies in the oldest stratigraphic layer?

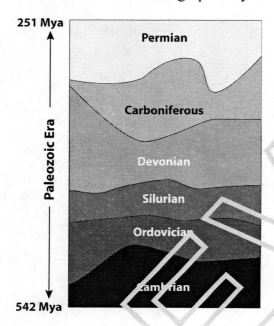

251 Mya

Paleozoic Era

- Permian
- Carboniferous
- Devonian
- Silurian
- Ordovician
- Cambrian

542 Mya

A. Cambrian dolostone

B. Cambro-Ordovician dolostone

C. Ordovician limestone

D. Carboniferous sandstone

Use the following diagram to answer questions 2 – 4.

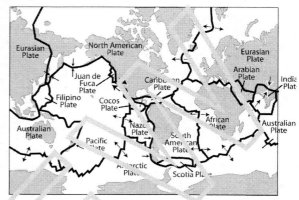

2. Along the western coast of South America, the oceanic Nazca plate is being pushed under the continental South American plate. What is an accurate term for the resulting geologic formation?

A. a continental-oceanic subduction zone

B. a continental-continental subduction zone

C. seafloor spreading

D. continental drift

3. There are 17 major tectonic plates on Earth. Which of the following is a true statement about these plates?

A. Every tectonic plate contains a continent.

B. Every tectonic plate contains continental crust.

C. Every tectonic plate contains oceanic crust.

D. Every tectonic plate is spreading.

4. When two oceanic plates converge, one plate is pushed below the other, often creating volcanic island arcs. Which landform is most likely the result of this process?

   A. Florida, in the North American Plate

   B. Great Britain, in the Eurasian Plate

   C. Japan, at the boundary of the Eurasian, North American and Filipino Plates

   D. Mexico, at the boundary of the Cocos and North American Plates.

5. What is the only geologic layer that is liquid?

   A. upper mantle

   B. lower mantle

   C. outer core

   D. inner core

6. Plate movement is thought to be caused by convection currents in the

   A. mantle.

   B. crust.

   C. outer core.

   D. inner core.

Use the following diagram to answer questions 7 – 9.

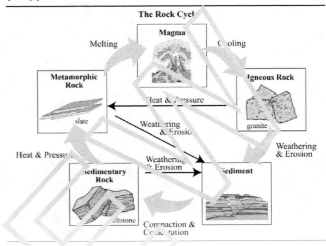

7. What is the only type of rock produced by cooling?

   A. igneous

   B. sedimentary

   C. metamorphic

   D. magma

8. Which of the following transitions does NOT happen in the rock cycle?

   A. Weathering and erosion convert igneous rock to sediment.

   B. Heat and pressure convert igneous rock to metamorphic rock.

   C. Weathering and erosion convert metamorphic rock to sediment.

   D. Heat and pressure convert metamorphic rock to igneous rock.

9. What is the only type of rock that is NOT produced by either heating or cooling?

   A. igneous

   B. sedimentary

   C. metamorphic

   D. magma

10. Ivy grows onto the walls of buildings by pushing its roots into fissures in the stone or brick. This is an example of

A. mechanical weathering.

B. biological weathering.

C. chemical weathering.

D. erosion.

11. Earthquakes are the common result of

A. plates pushing together at convergent boundaries.

B. plates pulling apart at convergent boundries.

C. plates pulling apart at divergent boundaries.

D. plates rubbing against each other at transform boundaries.

12. Earth's core is a very dense structure consisting mainly of

A. iron and carbon.

B. iron, nickel and carbon.

C. iron and nickel.

D. nickel and carbon.

13. Molten rock and metal from the mantle is transported outward until it meets the Earth's crust. At that point, it travels in a horizontal direction that may

A. cause movement of the outer core.

B. cause movement of tectonic plates.

C. cause the Coriolis force.

D. alter the gravitational pull of the Earth's core.

14. Trilobites were an extremely large and diverse group of animal species that became extinct about 250 million years ago. They were generally small and obtained food by filtering mud and sediment. They are almost always found fossilized alongside corals and brachiopods. Which of the following areas would be most likely to contain trilobite fossils?

A. area A   C. area C

B. area B   D. area D

15. Acid rain is primarily caused by pollution, including nitrogen oxides and sulfur dioxides. These chemicals are produced by the burning of fossil fuels. One of the negative effects of acid rain is that it lowers the pH of bodies of water, particularly lakes. Most fish eggs will not hatch at pH values lower than 5. If left unchecked, lake acidity results in the eventual death of lake ecosystems. What is the most effective long-term solution for decreasing the effects of acid rain?

A. Pumping the acidic water out of the lake and replacing it with clean water will help restore the neutral pH and leave the ecosystem undamaged.

B. Adding basic chemicals (pH greater than 7) to acidified lakes will lessen the acidity of the lake to a neutral level (pH of 7)

C. Stocking the lake with species of fish and amphibians that tolerate acidic water will create new ecosystems.

D. Decreasing fossil fuel emissions will decrease acid rain and allow the water cycle to gradually restore the lake to a neutral pH.

16. Stone Mountain is the largest exposed piece of granite in the world. It formed as a result of an upwelling of magma in the asthenosphere. The magma solidified to granite well below the Earth's surface. Which of the following terms describes Stone Mountain?

A. a volcano

B. intrusive igneous rock

C. extrusive igneous rock

D. a guyot

17. The United States considers plastic products disposable. In other words, as soon as a plastic container is emptied, a diaper is soiled, or a toy is broken, it is discarded and then sent to a landfill. Plastics are composed of polymers — long chains of molecules bound together. Decay organisms cannot penetrate these structures easily. Therefore, plastics take nearly 200 years to break down. Because of their molecular structure and the wide variety of different plastics available, they are also very difficult and expensive to recycle. What is a reasonable solution to the plastic problem that takes into account ecological, social, and economic factors?

A. Immediately stop the manufacture of all plastic products.

B. Pull all of the plastic out of existing landfills, recycle it and make no more plastic from raw materials.

C. Develop plastics using renewable resources, such as plant products, that decomposers can penetrate and break down.

D. Encourage consumers to stop purchasing any products made from or packaged in plastic until all plastic manufacturers are forced out of business.

18. The carbon cycle circulates carbon between the biosphere, geosphere, hydrosphere and atmosphere. Oil is a nonrenewable energy source that is slowly produced by the action of the carbon cycle in the geosphere. This means that

A. oil can never be replaced once it is depleted.

B. if the oil supply is depleted, it will take a very long time to build up again.

C. humans are free to use as much as they need because the carbon cycle will replenish the oil.

D. oil can be replaced in the lifetime of a human.

19. By law, construction sites are not allowed to pollute or disturb the area surrounding them. On paper this seems reasonable, but is more difficult in practice. One key feature of any construction site is that it is surrounded by a perimeter of sandbags and gravel. What is this perimeter designed to eliminate?

A. the spread of chemicals into surrounding areas

B. the loss of construction materials, such as nails, from the site

C. the erosion of exposed topsoil into surrounding areas

D. the trespass of animals and people onto the site

20. Convection currents in the Earth's mantle cause

A. the movement of the tectonic plates.

B. the alteration of weather patterns.

C. fluctuation of the gravitational pull from the core.

D. mechanical weathering of the lithosphere.

Georgia 6th Grade Science CRCT
Post Test 1

Post Test 1   Answer Sheet

Name: _____

Section 1

1. Ⓐ Ⓑ Ⓒ Ⓓ
2. Ⓐ Ⓑ Ⓒ Ⓓ
3. Ⓐ Ⓑ Ⓒ Ⓓ
4. Ⓐ Ⓑ Ⓒ Ⓓ
5. Ⓐ Ⓑ Ⓒ Ⓓ
6. Ⓐ Ⓑ Ⓒ Ⓓ
7. Ⓐ Ⓑ Ⓒ Ⓓ
8. Ⓐ Ⓑ Ⓒ Ⓓ
9. Ⓐ Ⓑ Ⓒ Ⓓ
10. Ⓐ Ⓑ Ⓒ Ⓓ
11. Ⓐ Ⓑ Ⓒ Ⓓ
12. Ⓐ Ⓑ Ⓒ Ⓓ
13. Ⓐ Ⓑ Ⓒ Ⓓ
14. Ⓐ Ⓑ Ⓒ Ⓓ
15. Ⓐ Ⓑ Ⓒ Ⓓ
16. Ⓐ Ⓑ Ⓒ Ⓓ
17. Ⓐ Ⓑ Ⓒ Ⓓ
18. Ⓐ Ⓑ Ⓒ Ⓓ
19. Ⓐ Ⓑ Ⓒ Ⓓ
20. Ⓐ Ⓑ Ⓒ Ⓓ
21. Ⓐ Ⓑ Ⓒ Ⓓ

22. Ⓐ Ⓑ Ⓒ Ⓓ
23. Ⓐ Ⓑ Ⓒ Ⓓ
24. Ⓐ Ⓑ Ⓒ Ⓓ
25. Ⓐ Ⓑ Ⓒ Ⓓ
26. Ⓐ Ⓑ Ⓒ Ⓓ
27. Ⓐ Ⓑ Ⓒ Ⓓ
28. Ⓐ Ⓑ Ⓒ Ⓓ
29. Ⓐ Ⓑ Ⓒ Ⓓ
30. Ⓐ Ⓑ Ⓒ Ⓓ

Section 2

31. Ⓐ Ⓑ Ⓒ Ⓓ
32. Ⓐ Ⓑ Ⓒ Ⓓ
33. Ⓐ Ⓑ Ⓒ Ⓓ
34. Ⓐ Ⓑ Ⓒ Ⓓ
35. Ⓐ Ⓑ Ⓒ Ⓓ
36. Ⓐ Ⓑ Ⓒ Ⓓ
37. Ⓐ Ⓑ Ⓒ Ⓓ
38. Ⓐ Ⓑ Ⓒ Ⓓ
39. Ⓐ Ⓑ Ⓒ Ⓓ
40. Ⓐ Ⓑ Ⓒ Ⓓ

41. Ⓐ Ⓑ Ⓒ Ⓓ
42. Ⓐ Ⓑ Ⓒ Ⓓ
43. Ⓐ Ⓑ Ⓒ Ⓓ
44. Ⓐ Ⓑ Ⓒ Ⓓ
45. Ⓐ Ⓑ Ⓒ Ⓓ
46. Ⓐ Ⓑ Ⓒ Ⓓ
47. Ⓐ Ⓑ Ⓒ Ⓓ
48. Ⓐ Ⓑ Ⓒ Ⓓ
49. Ⓐ Ⓑ Ⓒ Ⓓ
50. Ⓐ Ⓑ Ⓒ Ⓓ
51. Ⓐ Ⓑ Ⓒ Ⓓ
52. Ⓐ Ⓑ Ⓒ Ⓓ
53. Ⓐ Ⓑ Ⓒ Ⓓ
54. Ⓐ Ⓑ Ⓒ Ⓓ
55. Ⓐ Ⓑ Ⓒ Ⓓ
56. Ⓐ Ⓑ Ⓒ Ⓓ
57. Ⓐ Ⓑ Ⓒ Ⓓ
58. Ⓐ Ⓑ Ⓒ Ⓓ
59. Ⓐ Ⓑ Ⓒ Ⓓ
60. Ⓐ Ⓑ Ⓒ Ⓓ

Section 1

Use the illustration to answer question 1

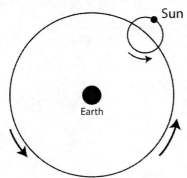

Sun

Earth

1. Which theory does the illustration
   describe?   S6E1a

   A. Geocentric theory

   B. Heliocentric theory

   C. Big Bang theory

   D. Continental drift theory

2. If the distance from the Sun to   S6CS3a, S6E1b
   the center of the galaxy is
   approximately 30,000 light years, about what
   distance would this be in kilometers?

   A. 3,000 million   C. 300,000 million

   B. 3,000 trillion   D. 300,000 trillion

3. Common marram grass is often   S6E5i
   planted by humans on beach dunes.
   Which of the following would be the best
   reason for this intentional planting?

   A. to increase dune erosion

   B. to decrease dune erosion

   C. to increase sand weathering and create
   soil

   D. to decrease sand weathering and create
   soil

4. Mars is a terrestrial planet,   S6CS3d, S6E1c
   about half the size of Earth,
   with an average surface temperature of
   -81°F. Venus is a terrestrial planet about the
   same size as Earth, with an average surface
   temperature of 867°F. What is the main
   reason why scientists think that water and
   possibly even life may be found on Mars, but
   not on Venus?

   A. Venus is too much like Earth to support
   life.

   B. Venus is a Gas Giant, and is therefore
   uninhabitable.

   C. Venus is far too hot to support life.

   D. Venus is far too cold to support any life.

5. Water can exist on Earth as a   S6E6a

   A. solid only.

   B. liquid only.

   C. gas only.

   D. solid, liquid or gas.

6. Which of the following words   S6E2a
   means "increasing" when talking
   about the phases of the moon?

   A. waning   C. waxing

   B. rising   D. diminishing

PLEASE GO ON TO THE NEXT PAGE ⟶

Use the illustration to answer question 7.

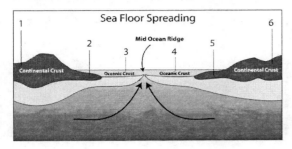

Sea Floor Spreading

7. Which areas on the illustration   S6E5f
   represent the oldest rocks?

   A. 2 and 3   C. 1 and 6

   B. 3 and 4   D. 4 and 5

Use the illustration to answer question 8.

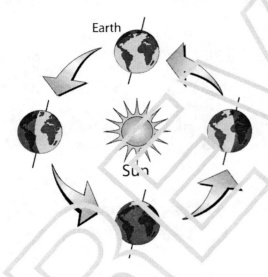

8. What motion of the Earth does the   S6E1d
   picture above best illustrate?

   A. Earth's rotation

   B. Earth's alternation

   C. Earth's constellation

   D. Earth's revolution

9. Water takes up the Sun's energy   S6E4a

   A. faster than the air.

   B. slower than the air.

   C. at the same rate as the air.

   D. at a continuous rate.

10. Gravity is a pulling force that acts   S6E1e
    over distance. What would happen
    to the force of the gravitational pull between
    the Earth and the Sun if the mass of the Earth
    decreased, but the distance from the Earth to
    the Sun remained the same?

    A. The pull of gravity would decrease.

    B. The pull of gravity would increase.

    C. The pull of gravity would not change.

    D. The pull of gravity would no longer exist.

11. The solar system is thought to have   S6E1a
    been formed from which of the
    following?

    A. the Sun   C. a black hole

    B. a galaxy   D. a nebula

12. What causes the Moon to appear to   S6E2a
    glow?

    A. The Moon produces its own light.

    B. The Moon reflects the light from the
       Earth.

    C. The Moon reflects the light from the Sun.

    D. The Moon reflects the light from the stars.

13. The theory of plate tectonics   S6E5f
    describes movements of plates. The
    movement originates in the

    A. inner core.   C. mantle.

    B. outer core.   D. crust.

14. What is a hypothesis?   S6E5e

   A. an idea that can be tested by experimentation and observation

   B. an undisputed fact

   C. a law of science

   D. a speculation not based on observation

15. If the Earth's speed of rotation were to suddenly decrease, what would happen to the length of the seasons?   S6E2c

   A. They would remain about the same.

   B. They would be shorter.

   C. They would be longer.

   D. There would only be two seasons.

16. Galileo observed that Venus is like Earth's Moon in one way. How are these two celestial bodies similar?   S6CS5a, S6E1c

   A. They are both part of the Earth's orbit.

   B. They are both planets.

   C. They are both stars.

   D. They both go through visible phases.

Use the graph below to answer question 17.

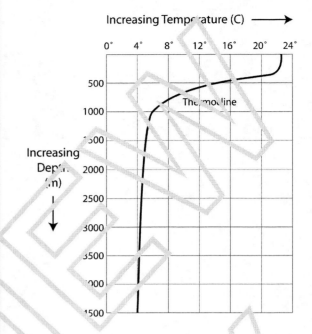

17. You are given this graph and asked to determine which ocean it is MOST LIKELY to represent. You know that 22°C is equal to 72°F. You conclude that this graph must represent the   S6E3a

   A. Arctic Ocean.

   B. Pacific Ocean near Washington state.

   C. Atlantic Ocean near Brazil.

   D. Atlantic Ocean near Maine.

18. Which rock group forms from the hardening of magma?   S6E5c

   A. sedimentary   C. obsidian

   B. metamorphic   D. igneous

PLEASE GO ON TO THE NEXT PAGE ⟶

19. Which of the following is the most constructive conservation method?   S6E5j

A. reduce paper use by writing on recycled plastic instead

B. reduce water use by drinking saved rainwater

C. reduce water use by watering lawns and gardens with saved rainwater

D. reduce energy use by using your fireplace more frequently in winter

20. If gravity did not act on the Earth, it would tend to move in straight line. This is part of Isaac Newton's First Law of Motion. What did Newton call this tendency?   S6E1e

A. centripetal force

B. tensional force

C. gravitational force

D. inertia

21. Condensation is responsible for the formation of   S6E3b

A. atmospheric wind.

B. clouds.

C. transpiration.

D. evaporation.

22. Echo sounding reports a sub-surface land form that takes 15 seconds to make a round trip. What is the MOST LIKELY landform represented by the echo sounding?   S6E3c

A. seamount

B. guyot

C. deep-sea trench

D. underwater volcano

23. How fast do sound waves travel in water?   S6E3c

A. 1,520 km/s

B. 1,520 m/s

C. 1,520 m/h

D. 1,520 km/h

24. What would happen if the rate of Earth's revolution increased?   S6E1d

A. The rotation of the Earth would also increase.

B. The number of days in a year would decrease.

C. The number of days in a year would increase.

D. There would be no change.

25. A wave's size is dependent on   S6E3d

A. the gravitational pull of the moon.

B. the speed of the wind, how long the wind blows and the distance the wind travels.

C. the speed of the wind and the distance the wind travels.

D. the gravitational pull of the sun.

26. Which of the rock groups is the most commonly found on Earth's surface?   S6E5c

A. magma

B. metamorphic

C. igneous

D. sedimentary

27. Which shape best illustrates the orientation of a comet's gas tail as it moves closer to the sun?   S6E1f

A.

B.

C.

D.

28. The Gulf Stream is caused by   S6E3

A. prevailing winds that occur regularly.

B. prevailing winds that occur irregularly.

C. strong storms.

D. the gravitational pull of the moon.

Use the illustration below to answer question 29.

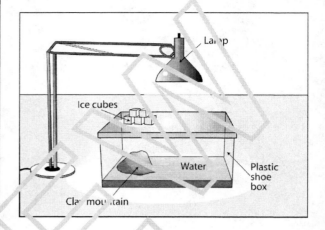

29. As part of a class assignment you set   S6E3b
up a model of the water cycle to determine how various atmospheric conditions relate to stages of the water cycle. From this model, which part of the water cycle represents condensation?

A. Condensation occurred as the water vapor from the "ocean" cooled on the lid of the shoebox near the ice.

B. Condensation was simulated as the "ocean" was heated by the lamp.

C. The drops of water falling from the lid of the shoebox simulated condensation.

D. Condensation was simulated by the water contained in the clay.

30. A scientist at an observatory is expecting to see a solar eclipse. He explains to visitors why a solar eclipse can only occur during a new moon. What does he say?

S6E2b

A. This is the only time that the Sun, the Moon and the Earth are directly lined up with the Earth between the Sun and the Moon.

B. This is the only time that the Sun, the Moon and the Earth are directly lined up with the Sun between the Earth and the Moon.

C. This is the only time that the Sun, the Moon and the Earth are directly lined up with the Moon between the Sun and the Earth.

D. This is the only time that the Sun, the Moon and the Earth are directly in line with one another.

Please STOP!

Do not go on to the next page!

Section 2

31. Which statement BEST describes the similarities between weather and climate?   S6E4a

    A. They both occur over long periods of time.

    B. They both occur over short periods of time.

    C. They are both affected by the Sun.

    D. They are the same globally.

32. During the first day of which season does Georgia experience its longest day?   S6E2c

    A. Winter   C. Summer

    B. Spring   D. Fall

33. \Which statement best describes the source of global wind patterns?   S6E4b

    A. Air circulates between the equator and the poles because of differences in air pressure, density and oxygen content.

    B. Air circulates between the equator and the poles because of differences in air pressure and density.

    C. Air circulates between the equator and the poles because of differences in air density and oxygen content.

    D. Air is pushed from the equator to the poles because of differences in air density and oxygen content.

34. What are the two main causes of mechanical weathering of a surface?   S6E5d

    A. chemical reactions and wind

    B. wind and water

    C. chemical reactions and water

    D. wind and acid rain

35. Construction adds to erosion by   S6E5i

    A. creating areas of drought.

    B. adding soil to the area.

    C. removing plant cover from the soil.

    D. adding plant cover to the soil.

36. From what does a hurricane derive its energy?   S6E4c

    A. Water heated by the Sun evaporates from the ocean's surface.

    B. Moist air heated by the Sun condenses into the ocean.

    C. Cool, moist air evaporates from the ocean's surface.

    D. Cool, dry air evaporates from the ocean's surface.

37. Where is most of Earth's fresh water found?   S6E3a

    A. rivers   C. streams

    B. lakes   D. glaciers

Use the diagram to answer question 38

38. The column of low pressure and no winds down the middle of this hurricane is known as   S6E4c

    A. the eye.   C. the nucleus.

    B. the core.   D. the pivot.

PLEASE GO ON TO THE NEXT PAGE ⟶

39. Erosion by gravity is MOST LIKELY to   S6E5d

    A. create a valley.

    B. wear away a beach.

    C. move a sand dune.

    D. cause a landslide.

Use the diagram to answer question 40

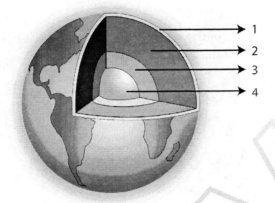

40. In which layers of the Earth would you expect to find solid material?   S6E5a

    A. 1 and 2   C. 3 and 4

    B. 2 and 3   D. 1 and 4

41. About how many days after the full moon appears in the sky will you expect to see the new moon?   S6E2a

    A. 5   B. 10   C. 15   D. 20

42. Which of the following describes how Earth's lithospheric plates move?   S6E5f

    A. plate tectonics

    B. plate vibration

    C. plate progression

    D. plate deformation

43. Hurricanes continue to grow and move as long as they continue to be   S6E4c

    A. over warm ocean water.

    B. over cool ocean water.

    C. pushed along by wind currents.

    D. pushed along by water currents.

44. What is the scientific name for a shooting star?   S6E1f

    A. comet   C. meteor

    B. asteroid   D. meteoroid

45. What type of material would you expect to find in the inner core of the Earth?   S6E5a, S6E5b

    A. solid rock composed of silicon, oxygen, aluminum, iron and sodium

    B. liquid rock composed of silicon, oxygen, aluminum, iron and sodium

    C. liquid rock composed of iron and nickel

    D. solid rock composed of iron and nickel

46. What weather phenomenon produces the lowest air pressures measured on Earth?   S6E4b

    A. hurricanes

    B. convection currents

    C. global currents

    D. tornadoes

47. Which of the following best illustrates the position of the Earth, Sun and Moon during a lunar eclipse? S6E2b

A.

B.

C.

D.

48. Where are the lithospheric plates located? S6E5e

A. the inner core

B. the outer core and mantle

C. the mantle and inner core

D. the crust and upper mantle

49. What do the following human activities all have in common? S6E5j

strip-mining, clear-cutting, open-pit mining

A. They are all environmentally friendly.

B. They all pollute the environment.

C. They all increase soil erosion.

D. They are all forms of mining.

50. Scientists have found fossils of coral in the Arctic Ocean. Coral requires warm water in order to live. What does this fossil finding tell us about Earth's past? S6E5g

A. The climate of Earth was once warmer.

B. The climate of the Earth was once cooler.

C. The Arctic Ocean moved from a warm climate to a cool climate by seafloor spreading.

D. The Arctic Ocean moved from a cool climate to a warm climate by seafloor spreading.

51. The summer solstice is on or around June 21st. In Atlanta, GA, summer solstice is S6E2c

A. the shortest day of the year.

B. the shortest day of the month

C. the longest day of the year.

D. the warmest day of the year.

Use the illustration to answer question 52.

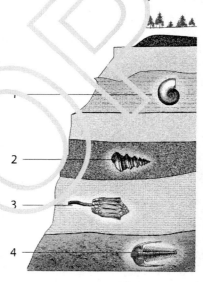

52. Which fossil is the oldest? S6E5g

A. 1   B. 2   C. 3   D. 4

PLEASE GO ON TO THE NEXT PAGE ⟶

Use the diagram below to answer question 53.

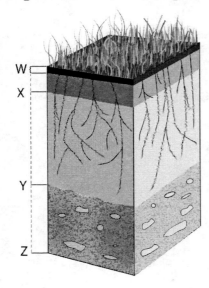

53. Which letter on the above illustration represents the B horizon, also known as subsoil?   S6E5h

   A. W   B. X   C. Y   D. Z

54. How does energy reach the Earth?   S6E6a

   A. lunar winds

   B. evapotranspiration

   C. solar flares

   D. radiation

55. An astronomical unit is a measure of   S6E1b

   A. speed.   C. distance.

   B. volume.   D. area.

56. The South Atlantic Ocean seafloor spreads at a rate of about 5 cm a year. How many years will it take for the seafloor to spread 3 feet (about 90 centimeters)?   S6E5i

   A. 1.8 years   C. 180 years

   B. 18 years   D. 1,800 years

Use the graph to answer question 57.

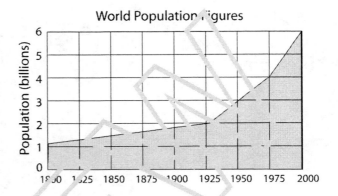

57. Between which years did Earth's population more than double?   S6E6b

   A. 1800 – 1850

   B. 1850 – 1900

   C. 1900 – 1950

   D. 1950 – 2000

58. Which of the following is NOT considered a major planet?   S6E1c

   A. Pluto   C. Uranus

   B. Mercury   D. Neptune

59. Upper layers of rock are generally   S6E5g

   A. older than lower layers of rock.

   B. the same age as all rock layers.

   C. the same density as lower layers of rock.

   D. younger than lower layers of rock.

PLEASE GO ON TO THE NEXT PAGE ⟶

60. Which series of pictures BEST represents the theory of continental drift, from Pangaea to the present day arrangement of continents?   S6E5e

A.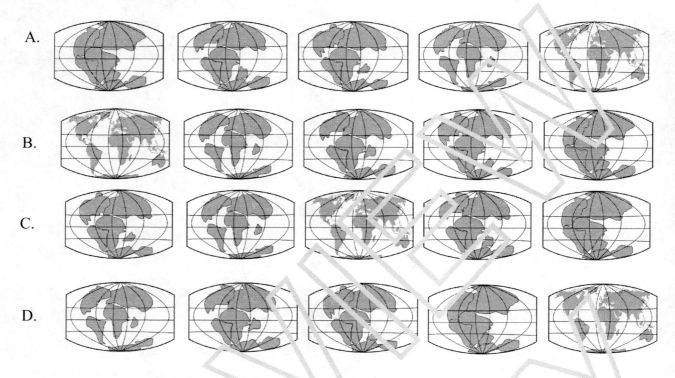

B.

C.

D.

Please STOP!

Do not go on to the next page!

Georgia 6th Grade CRCT in Science
Post Test 2

Post Test 2   **Answer Sheet**

Name: _____

Section 1

1. (A) (B) (C) (D)
2. (A) (B) (C) (D)
3. (A) (B) (C) (D)
4. (A) (B) (C) (D)
5. (A) (B) (C) (D)
6. (A) (B) (C) (D)
7. (A) (B) (C) (D)
8. (A) (B) (C) (D)
9. (A) (B) (C) (D)
10. (A) (B) (C) (D)
11. (A) (B) (C) (D)
12. (A) (B) (C) (D)
13. (A) (B) (C) (D)
14. (A) (B) (C) (D)
15. (A) (B) (C) (D)
16. (A) (B) (C) (D)
17. (A) (B) (C) (D)
18. (A) (B) (C) (D)
19. (A) (B) (C) (D)
20. (A) (B) (C) (D)
21. (A) (B) (C) (D)

22. (A) (B) (C) (D)
23. (A) (B) (C) (D)
24. (A) (B) (C) (D)
25. (A) (B) (C) (D)
26. (A) (B) (C) (D)
27. (A) (B) (C) (D)
28. (A) (B) (C) (D)
29. (A) (B) (C) (D)
30. (A) (B) (C) (D)

Section 2

31. (A) (B) (C) (D)
32. (A) (B) (C) (D)
33. (A) (B) (C) (D)
34. (A) (B) (C) (D)
35. (A) (B) (C) (D)
36. (A) (B) (C) (D)
37. (A) (B) (C) (D)
38. (A) (B) (C) (D)
39. (A) (B) (C) (D)
40. (A) (B) (C) (D)

41. (A) (B) (C) (D)
42. (A) (B) (C) (D)
43. (A) (B) (C) (D)
44. (A) (B) (C) (D)
45. (A) (B) (C) (D)
46. (A) (B) (C) (D)
47. (A) (B) (C) (D)
48. (A) (B) (C) (D)
49. (A) (B) (C) (D)
50. (A) (B) (C) (D)
51. (A) (B) (C) (D)
52. (A) (B) (C) (D)
53. (A) (B) (C) (D)
54. (A) (B) (C) (D)
55. (A) (B) (C) (D)
56. (A) (B) (C) (D)
57. (A) (B) (C) (D)
58. (A) (B) (C) (D)
59. (A) (B) (C) (D)
60. (A) (B) (C) (D)

Section 1

1. What theory explains the creation of the universe? `S6E1a`

   A. the Heliocentric theory

   B. the Initial Bang theory

   C. the Big Bang Theory

   D. the Geocentric theory

2. Limestone, under heat and pressure, forms marble. What type of rock is marble? `S6E5c`

   A. sedimentary   C. igneous

   B. metamorphic   D. magma

3. What factor most influences a planet's average temperatures? `S6E1c`

   A. atmospheric composition

   B. distance from the Sun

   C. size

   D. both A and B

4. What is a pollutant? `S6E5j`

   A. harmful substances in air, water or soil

   B. harmful substances in air

   C. harmful substances in water

   D. harmful substances in soil

5. Which of the following is considered a renewable resource? `S6E6b`

   A. petroleum   C. metal

   B. wood   D. natural gas

6. Which of the following illustrations best represents the idea of revolution? `S6E1d`

   A.

   B.

   C.
   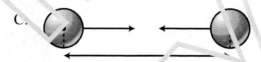

   D.

7. A cyclone forms as a result of a `S6E4c`

   A. cold front.

   B. warm front.

   C. stationary front.

   D. occluded front.

8. The effects of gravity are different on each planet. If you know that your dog weighs 30 kg on Earth, how much would the dog weigh on Uranus, which has 90% of the Earth's gravity? `S6E1c`

   A. 33.3 kg   C. 18 kg

   B. 27.0 kg   D. 66 kg

PLEASE GO ON TO THE NEXT PAGE ⟶

Use the image to answer question 9.

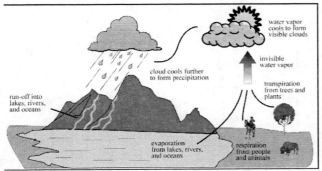

9. Which element of the water cycle is not labeled on the diagram above?   S6E6a

   A. groundwater flow

   B. overland flow

   C. rain

   D. evapotranspiration

Use the data below to answer question 10

Planet	Distance between Sun and planet	Product of Masses of Sun and planet
1	58 million km	6.6×10^{53} kg
2	108 million km	5.8×10^{54} kg
3	149 million km	1.2×10^{55} kg
4	4 billion km	2.6×10^{52} kg

10. You collect the above data through an Internet search. From this data, you conclude that   S6E1e

    A. gravity has the least effect on planet 1.

    B. gravity has the most effect on planet 3.

    C. gravity has the least effect on planet 4.

    D. gravity has the most effect on planet 2.

11. Which illustrations best describes the position of the Earth, Sun and Moon during the new moon phase?   S6E2a

   A.

   B.

   C.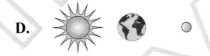

   D.

12. What factors affect the force of gravity between two objects?   S6E1e

    A. distance between the two objects

    B. the product of their masses

    C. both the distance between the objects and product of their masses

    D the difference in mass between the two objects

13. What causes a solar eclipse?   S6E2b

    A. The Moon passes between the Sun and the Earth.

    B. The Earth passes between the Moon and the Sun.

    C. The Sun passes between the Moon and the Earth.

    D. An asteroid passes between the Sun and the Earth.

14. What condition must hold true for either a lunar or solar eclipse to occur? **S6E2b**

   A. The Moon must be in the new phase.

   B. The Sun, Moon and Earth must be on the same plane.

   C. The Sun and the Earth must be on the same plane.

   D. The Moon and the Earth must be on the same plane.

15. How much of the Earth is covered in water? **S6E3a**

   A. 30%   C. 70%

   B. 50%   D. 90%

16. About how many days does each season last? **S6E2c**

   A. 91   C. 273

   B. 182   D. 365

Use the illustration below to answer question 17.

17. Which ocean is marked by an "X" in the illustration above? **S6E3a**

   A. Atlantic   C. Indian

   B. Pacific   D. Arctic

18. Which form of salt is most dominant in the world's oceans? **S6E3c**

   A. sodium chloride (NaCl)

   B. calcium chloride (CaCl)

   C. potassium chloride (KCl)

   D. magnesium chloride (MgCl)

19. What does Earth's rotation do to global wind patterns? **S6E4b**

   A. It causes the winds to move straight north and straight south.

   B. It causes the winds to move counter clockwise in the Northern Hemisphere and clockwise in the Southern Hemisphere.

   C. It causes the winds to move clockwise in the Northern Hemisphere and counter clockwise in the Southern Hemisphere.

   D. It causes the winds to move in a clockwise direction globally.

20. What is the main difference between an asteroid and a meteoroid? **S6E1f**

   A. size   C. material

   B. shape   D. age

21. Two identical fossils were found in North America and Africa. What can you assume from this information? **S6E5e**

   A. Africa and North America were once joined.

   B. The evidence does not support the theory of plate tectonics.

   C. There was once a large migration of animals across the ocean.

   D. The evidence does not support the theory of continental drift.

PLEASE GO ON TO THE NEXT PAGE ⟶

Use the chart below to answer question 22

Wind Speed and Waves		
Wind Speed (km/hr)	Average Wave Height (m)	Average Length (m)
20	0.33	10.6
40	1.8	39.7
60	5.1	89.2
80	10.3	158.6

22. If the wind speed were to decrease, what would happen to wave height and length? S6E3d

   A. The height would increase and the length would increase.

   B. The height would decrease and the length would decrease.

   C. The height would decrease and the length increase.

   D. The height would increase and the length decrease.

23. What is another common name for mature hurricanes and typhoons? S6E4c

   A. tropical depression

   B. tropical storm

   C. tornado

   D. tropical cyclone

24. What would happen to the seasons if the Earth were not tilted at a 23.5° angle? S6E2c

   A. The Earth would have more seasons than at present.

   B. The Earth would have no seasons.

   C. The Earth would have the same number of seasons as now.

   D. The Earth would have shorter seasons.

25. Tides are affected by the S6E3d

   A. Earth's gravity and wind.

   B. Sun's gravity and Moon's gravity.

   C. Sun's gravity and Earth's gravity.

   D. Moon's gravity and wind.

26. What fraction of the Moon is seen during the Third Quarter phase? S6E2a

   A. 1/2   C. 1/3

   B. 1/4   D. 3/4

27. A meteorologist states that a cold front is moving into north Georgia from the south. This means that the air mass moving into north Georgia S6E4a

   A. is colder and drier than the air mass it replaces.

   B. is warmer and drier than the air mass it replaces.

   C. is colder and wetter than the air mass it replaces.

   D. is warmer and wetter than the air mass it replaces.

28. Which of the following is NOT part of the subsurface topography of the world's oceans? S6E3c

   A. continental crust

   B. deep-sea trench

   C. volcano

   D. mountain range

29. Which of the following BEST describes the layers of the Earth from hottest to coolest?   S6E5a

   A. mantle, crust, inner core, outer core.

   B. inner core, mantle, crust, outer core.

   C. outer core, inner core, crust, mantle.

   D. inner core, outer core, mantle, crust.

30. Which layer of the Earth is the thinnest?   S6E5a

   A. crust   C. outer core

   B. mantle   D. inner core

Please STOP!

Do not go on to the next page!

Section 2

31. Which statement best describes a tornado? S6E4b

    A. swiftly turning, very high-pressure funnel of air

    B. swiftly turning, very low-pressure funnel of air

    C. slowly turning, very high-pressure funnel of air

    D. slowly turning, very low-pressure funnel of air

32. What energy source is essential for the water cycle to work? S6E3

    A. wind   C. lunar

    B. solar   D. mechanical

Use the diagram to answer questions 33 and 34.

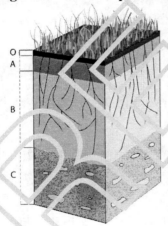

33. In which soil horizon would you be most likely to find earthworms? S6E5h

    A. the A horizon   C. the C horizon

    B. the B horizon   D. the O horizon

34. Which horizon contains both bedrock and weathered bedrock? S6E5h

    A. O horizon   C. B horizon

    B. A horizon   D. C horizon

35. If high tide in Savannah, Georgia occurs at 7:30 AM on May 11th. When will the next high tide occur? S6E3d

    A. 12:45 PM

    B. 1:36 PM

    C. 7:55 PM

    D. 8:11 PM

36. Hurricanes will typically lose strength S6E4c

    A. after about two weeks.

    B. once they make landfall or travel over cooler ocean water.

    C. once they reach speeds of approximately 165 mph.

    D. after the winds die down.

37. Which of the following is thought to have occurred first? S6E1a

    A. the formation of the Sun

    B. the Big Bang

    C. the formation of the Milky Way Galaxy

    D. the formation of the solar system

38. Which of the illustrations best describes convection currents? S6E4a

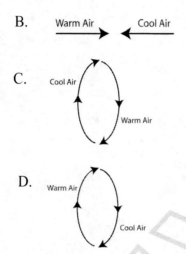

A.

Cool Air

Warm Air

B. Warm Air → ← Cool Air

C. Cool Air

Warm Air

D. Warm Air

Cool Air

39. How long does one revolution of the Earth take? S6E1d

A. 24 hours   C. an hour

B. 365 days   D. a month

40. If you were to discover a rock that appeared to have layers, what kind of rock would you suspect it to be? S6E5c

A. metamorphic   C. sedimentary

B. igneous   D. lava

41. What features on Earth are created when two continental plates collide? S6E5e

A. volcanic islands

B. trenches

C. mountains

D. volcanic mountains

42. Where are most asteroids located? S6E1f

A. between Venus and Earth

B. between Mars and Jupiter

C. between Mercury and Venus

D. between Earth and Mars

Use the illustration to answer question 43.

1 = Bedrock

2 = Silt and Clay

3 = Weathered rock fragments

4 = Organic matter

43. The illustration above represents a mixed-up soil profile. In which order should the layers be labeled from top to bottom? S6E5f

A. 4,2,3,1   C. 2,4,3,1

B. 1,3,2,4   D. 4,3,2,1

44. A convection current in a liquid system is described by S6E5f

A. less dense liquid moving down and more dense moving up.

B. more dense liquid moving down and less dense liquid moving up.

C. liquids of equal density moving up and down.

D. solids of equal density moving up and down in a liquid.

PLEASE GO ON TO THE NEXT PAGE ⟶

45. The Milky Way Galaxy is thickest in   S6E1b

   A. the center.

   B. the inner arms.

   C. our solar system.

   D. the outer arms.

46. Windbreaks and terracing help   S6E5j

   A. water stay on fields.

   B. soil stay on fields.

   C. keep pollutants on fields.

   D. improve the landscape.

47. Water on the Earth's surface can move as   S6E6a

   A. condensation.

   B. evaporation.

   C. runoff and groundwater.

   D. water vapor.

48. The distance between Savannah, Georgia and Morocco (in Africa) is about 7613 km (4730 miles). If the ocean floor has been spreading at a rate of about 5 cm per year, when did the Atlantic Ocean begin to form?   S6E5f

   A. 1,500 years ago

   B. 30,000 years ago

   C. 15,000,000 years ago

   D. 150,000,000 years ago

49. Finding shark's teeth in the desert would lead you to hypothesize that the desert was   S6E5g

   A. once covered by fresh water.

   B. once covered by salt water.

   C. once a mountain covered by fresh water.

   D. once a mountain covered by salt water.

50. Which type of erosion BEST describes what happened during the Dust Bowl in the 1930s?   S6E5i

   A. landslide erosion

   B. wind erosion

   C. wave erosion

   D. sheet and rill erosion

51. Which of the following is a source of renewable energy?   S6E6b

   A. wind   C. oil

   B. coal   D. natural gas

52. A drought is   S6E5i

   A. a period of heavy rainfall.

   B. a period of heavy winds.

   C. a period of light winds.

   D. a period of light rainfall.

53. About how long is one Moon cycle?   S6E2a

   A. one day   C. one year

   B. one hour   D. one month

54. Which of the following farm pollutants is/are MOST LIKELY to enter nearby waterways?   S6E5j

   A. gas from tractors

   B. food meant for livestock

   C. soil and fertilizers from a field

   D. manure from livestock

55. Stars appear to change position in the night sky because of the motion of the Earth. What factors below explain why the stars appear to move?   S6E1d

   A. rotation and revolution of the Earth around the Sun

   B. rotation and revolution of the stars around the Earth

   C. rotation and revolution of the Moon around the Sun

   D. rotation and revolution of the Sun around the Earth

56. A ship on the Atlantic Ocean pings a section of ocean floor. The ping is received 5 seconds after it is sent. About how deep is the ocean floor in this location?   S6E3c

   A. less than 1000 meters

   B. between 3,000 and 4,000 meters

   C. between 6,000 and 8,000 meters

   D. more than 10,000 meters

57. The number of years it takes for running water to erode a canyon the size of the Grand Canyon should be measured in   S6E5d

   A. hundreds of years.

   B. thousands of years.

   C. millions of years.

   D. billions of years.

58. If the spaceship *Endeavor* were able to travel from Earth to center of the Milky Way Galaxy at twice the speed of light, about how many years would it take to accomplish its mission?   S6E1b

   A. 15,000 years   C. 45,000 years

   B. 30,000 years   D. 60,000 years

59. U-shaped valleys are MOST LIKELY caused by erosion due to   S6E5d

   A. wind.   C. rivers.

   B. glaciers.   D. gravity.

60. Which of the following statements BEST describes the difference between weathering and erosion?   S6E5i

   A. Weathering involves both disintegration and movement of rocks.

   B. Erosion only applies to soil, not rocks.

   C. Erosion describes the movement of rocks.

   D. Weathering only applies to rocks, not soil.

A

air mass, 78
Alpha Centauri, 23
asteroid, 24
asthenosphere, 94
atmosphere, 59
autumnal equinox, 34

B

Big Bang theory, 17, 20
biological weathering, 107
biosphere, 59

C

chemical weathering, 107
climate
    factors of, 77
continental crust, 94, 97
continental drift, 98
convection current, 74, 98
convergent boundary, 99
Coriolis Effect, 75

D

divergent boundary, 99
dust bowl, 109

E

earth
    orbit, 33, 50
    systems, 59
earthquake, 100
eclipse
    moon, 46
    seasons, 46
electromagnetic wave, 51
energy
    wave, 51
equinox
    types of, 34
erosion, 108
expanding universe theory, 19
extrusive igneous rock, 103

F

fault, 100
fold
    plunging, 100
    rock, 100
fossil record, 90
fusion, 19

H

heat absorption rate, 74
hurricane, 80
    characteristics of, 80
hydrosphere, 59

I

IAU, 26
igneous rock, 104
    types of, 103
index fossil, 90
intrusive igneous rock, 103

J

Jovian planet, 25

L

lava, 103, 105
lithosphere, 59, 94
lunar eclipse, 46

M

magma, 103, 105
mechanical weathering, 107
metamorphic rock, 104
mid latitudes, 77
Milky Way, 19
moon
    phases, 41, 42

N

natural resource, 119
nebular hypothesis, 23
neutron, 17
non-renewable resource, 119
nuclear, 17

O

oceanic crust, 97
orbital plane, 33

P

Pangaea, 98
plate boundary, 105
    types of, 99
plate tectonic, 97
proton, 17
protoplanet, 24
protosun, 24

R

rate, 18
relative dating, 90

renewable resource, 119
rock
    cycle, 104
    types of, 103
rock strata, 90

S

seafloor spreading, 98
sediment, 104
sedimentary rock, 104
solar nebula, 23
solar radiation, 51
solar wind, 24
spring equinox, 34
subduction zone, 99
summer solstice, 34
sun
    energy, 73
surface ocean current, 75

T

tectonic plate, 94
terrestrial planet, 24
tide, 69
    moon and sun effect on, 70
TNO, 26
tornado alley, 80
transform boundary, 99
Tropic of Cancer, 34
Tropic of Capricorn, 34
tsunami, 108
typhoon, 80

V

vent, 105

W

water erosion, 108
weather
    factors of, 77
    types of, 107
weather front
    types of, 78, 79
winter solstice, 34

Product Order Form

Please fill this form out completely and fax it to 1-866-827-3240.

American Book Company
Meeting Standards, Exceeding Expectations

Purchase Order #: _____   Date: _____

Contact Person: _____

School Name (and District, if any): _____
_____

Billing Address: Street Address: ☐ same as billing
_____   _____

Attn: _____   Attn: _____
_____   _____
_____   _____

Phone: _____ E-Mail: _____

Credit Card #: _____ Exp Date: _____

Authorized Signature: _____

Order Number	Product Title	Pricing* 5 books	30 books	Total Cost
GA5-M0806	Mastering the Georgia 5th Grade CRCT in Mathematics	$49.95 (1 set of 5 books)	$254.70 (1 set of 30 books)	
GA5-R1206	Mastering the Georgia 5th Grade CRCT in Reading	$49.95 (1 set of 5 books)	$254.70 (1 set of 30 books)	
GA6-M0305	Mastering the Georgia 6th Grade CRCT in Mathematics	$49.95 (1 set of 5 books)	$254.70 (1 set of 30 books)	
GA6-S1206	Mastering the Georgia 6th Grade CRCT in Science	$49.95 (1 set of 5 books)	$254.70 (1 set of 30 books)	
GA7-M0305	Mastering the Georgia 7th Grade CRCT in Mathematics	$49.95 (1 set of 5 books)	$254.70 (1 set of 30 books)	
GA7-S1206	Mastering the Georgia 7th Grade CRCT in Science	$49.95 (1 set of 5 books)	$254.70 (1 set of 30 books)	
GA8-M0305	Passing the Georgia 8th Grade CRCT in Mathematics	$49.95 (1 set of 5 books)	$254.70 (1 set of 30 books)	
GA8-L0505	Passing the Georgia 8th Grade CRCT in Language Arts	$49.95 (1 set of 5 books)	$254.70 (1 set of 30 books)	
GA8-R0505	Passing the Georgia 8th Grade CRCT in Reading	$49.95 (1 set of 5 books)	$254.70 (1 set of 30 books)	
GAMG-W0805	Preparing for the Georgia Middle Grades Writing Assessment	$49.95 (1 set of 5 books)	$254.70 (1 set of 30 books)	
GA-EOCL0806	Passing the Georgia 9th Grade Lit. and Comp. End of Course	$54.95 (1 set of 5 books)	$284.70 (1 set of 30 books)	
GA-EOCM0904	Passing the Georgia Algebra I End of Course	$54.95 (1 set of 5 books)	$284.70 (1 set of 30 books)	
GA-EOCB0805	Passing the Georgia Biology End of Course	$54.95 (1 set of 5 books)	$284.70 (1 set of 30 books)	
GA-EOCE0305	Passing the Georgia Economics End of Course	$54.95 (1 set of 5 books)	$284.70 (1 set of 30 books)	
GA-EOCG0505	Passing the Georgia Geometry End of Course	$54.95 (1 set of 5 books)	$284.70 (1 set of 30 books)	
GA-EOCP0106	Passing the Georgia Physical Science End of Course	$54.95 (1 set of 5 books)	$284.70 (1 set of 30 books)	
GA-EOCH0605	Passing the Georgia United States History End of Course	$54.95 (1 set of 5 books)	$284.70 (1 set of 30 books)	
GA-L1206	Passing the Georgia English Language Arts Graduation Test	$69.95 (1 set of 5 books)	$374.70 (1 set of 30 books)	
GA-M0705	Passing the Georgia Mathematics Graduation Test	$69.95 (1 set of 5 books)	$374.70 (1 set of 30 books)	
GA-S0806	Passing the Georgia Science Graduation Test	$69.95 (1 set of 5 books)	$374.70 (1 set of 30 books)	
GA-H0300N	Passing the Georgia Social Studies Graduation Test	$69.95 (1 set of 5 books)	$374.70 (1 set of 30 books)	
GA-W1000N	Passing the Georgia Writing Graduation Test	$69.95 (1 set of 5 books)	$374.70 (1 set of 30 books)	
Call for Order #	Passing the Georgia Graduation Test On-Line Testing**	$399.00 (1 year subscription)		

1-5-07

*Minimum order is 1 set of 5 books of the same subject.
**Each subscription is per subject. Only $299 for customers who have previously purchased a site license! If you qualify, please call us today to secure your lower price!

Subtotal	
Shipping & Handling 10% (- $100 per subscription for previous customers**)	
Total	

American Book Company ● PO Box 2638 ● Woodstock, GA 30188-1383
Toll Free: 1-888-264-5877 ● Fax: 1-866-827-3240 ● Web Site: www.americanbookcompany.com